TEACHER'S RESOURCE MASTERS

BLACKLINE MASTERS AND TEACHER'S MANUAL

GRADE 1

SPOTLIGHT on MUSIC™

SERIES AUTHORS

Judy Bond

René Boyer

Margaret Campbelle-Holman

Emily Crocker

Marilyn C. Davidson

Robert de Frece

Virginia Ebinger

Mary Goetze

Betsy M. Henderson

John Jacobson

Michael Jothen

Chris Judah-Lauder

Carol King

Vincent P. Lawrence

Ellen McCullough-Brabson

Janet McMillion

Nancy L.T. Miller

Ivy Rawlins

Susan Snyder

Gilberto D. Soto

Kodály Contributing Consultant
Sr. Lorna Zemke

Macmillan McGraw-Hill

INTRODUCTION

This *Teacher's Resource Masters* book contains supplementary activities for *Spotlight on Music*. These Resource Masters include the following:

- A variety of activities that reinforce or review concepts taught in the lessons. Some Resource Masters emphasize manipulative activities, while others offer opportunities for written or aural activities.

- Student and teacher support to complete the Creative Unit Projects. Students can use the Resource Masters to guide them through the project and complete a self-assessment at the project's conclusion. Teachers are also given an assessment rubric for each Creative Unit Project.

- Listening maps that provide visual guidance for students as they listen to specific music selections. The listening maps help students identify melodic and rhythmic patterns, tone color, form, and other musical elements. Suggestions for how to use these listening maps in the classroom are provided at the beginning of the Listening Map section.

- Review questions for each unit. The Spotlight Your Success! Resource Masters allow students to record their responses to the review questions at the completion of each unit. The Read and Listen questions and music examples are recorded.

- Scripts and lyrics for this grade level's Broadway for Kids musical.

- Sign language versions of selected songs using American Sign Language.

All Resource Masters may be duplicated for classroom use. Each Resource Master is cross referenced to a specific unit and lesson that it was designed to support.

ACKNOWLEDGMENTS

Grateful acknowledgment is given to the following publishers. Every effort has been made to trace the ownership of all copyrighted material and to secure the necessary permissions to reprint these selections. In the case of some selections for which acknowledgment is not given, extensive research has failed to locate the copyright holders.

A YEAR WITH FROG AND TOAD JUNIOR
Music by Robert Reale   Book and Lyrics by Willie Reale
Based on the books by Arnold Lobel
Originally presented on Broadway by Bob Boyett, Adrianne Lobel, Michael Gardner, Lawrence Horowitz, and Roy Furman
World Premiere at The Children's Theater Company, Minneapolis, Minnesota

© Adrianne Lobel, Adam S. Lobel
and Robert Boyett Theatricals, LLC
A Year With Frog And Toad Junior Libretto/Vocal book
© 2004 by MTI Enterprises, Inc.
Broadway Junior and **The Broadway Junior Collection** are trademarks of MTI Enterprises, Inc.

Published by Macmillan/McGraw-Hill Education, a division of The McGraw-Hill Companies, Inc.,
Two Penn Plaza, New York, New York 10121

TABLE OF CONTENTS

SPOTLIGHT ON CONCEPTS

SPOTLIGHT ON MUSIC READING

SPOTLIGHT ON PERFORMANCE

SPOTLIGHT ON CELEBRATIONS

LISTENING MAPS

SPOTLIGHT ON SIGNING

School-to-Home Letter

RESOURCE MASTER 1•1

Dear Family,

Your child lives in a world full of musical sounds. From the steady ticking of a clock to the whistle of a passing train, rhythms and tones surround your first grader. Children are naturally drawn to the simple melodies of familiar songs and the rhythmic beat of nursery rhymes.

This unit will introduce several important musical concepts. Through listening exercises, games, and art projects, your child will learn about steady beats, melodic direction, and musical dynamics. These building blocks can provide the foundation for a lifetime of music appreciation.

You can help reinforce the lessons your child is learning by drawing attention to the rhythms and sounds you and your child experience in everyday life. You can point out the steady beat of the windshield wipers when you are driving through rain or help your child notice how the tone of a siren goes up and then down. While reading a poem aloud, you might tap out the strong beats of the poem. When singing a favorite song, try demonstrating singing it first in a loud voice and then in a whisper. Encourage your child to dance to the rhythm as she or he listens to music on the radio or on a CD—and you dance along, too!

Musically yours,

First Grade Music Teacher

School-to-Home Letter   RESOURCE MASTER   1•1

Estimada Familia:

Su hijo vive en un mundo lleno de sonidos musicales. Desde el firme tic-tac de un reloj al silbido de un tren que pasa, los ritmos y los tonos rodean a su pequeño de primer grado. Los niños se sienten atraídos por naturaleza con las simples melodías de las canciones familiares y la cadencia rítmica de las canciones de cuna.

Esta unidad presentará varios conceptos musicales importantes. Mediante ejercicios de audición, juegos y proyectos artísticos, su hijo aprenderá sobre los compases continuados, la dirección melódica y la dinámica musical. Estos 'ladrillos' pueden ofrecer los cimientos para que disfrute de la música para toda la vida.

Usted puede ayudar a su hijo a reforzar sus lecciones llamando su atención sobre los ritmos y sonidos que experimentan en la vida diaria. Usted puede señalarle el ritmo continuo del limpiaparabrisas cuando está conduciendo bajo la lluvia o puede ayudarle a prestar atención al modo en que el tono de una sirena aumenta y luego disminuye. Mientras lee un poema en voz alta, puede marcar los ritmos fuertes del mismo. Al cantar una de sus canciones favoritas, trate de hacerlo primero con una voz bien alta y luego en un murmullo. Aliente a su hijo a bailar siguiendo el ritmo cuando él o ella escuchen música de la radio o de un CD—y ¡baile usted a su lado, también!

Atentamente,

Maestra de Música de Primer Grado

Creative Unit Project

RESOURCE MASTER 1•2

Work with your group.
Keep the beat.
Follow these steps.

STEP 1
Look around.
What sounds have a steady beat?
What sounds have no steady beat?
Draw pictures.

steady beat	no steady beat

3

Creative Unit Project

RESOURCE MASTER 1•3

STEP 2
What sounds go
up and down?

What sounds stay
the same?

STEP 3
Remember STEP 1.
Look at your pictures.
Pick a sound that has
a steady beat.
Make up a movement for it.
Count 8 steady beats.

STEP 4
Pick a song.
Sing and move.
Use the song as the A section.
Use your 8 steady beats as the B section.
Perform as AB or ABA.

Steady or Not?

RESOURCE MASTER 1•4

Circle the things that make a steady beat.
Cross out the things that do not.

Name _____   Date _____

Names Up and Down

Write your name in the box. Then write your name going up into the clouds like a kite. Then write your name going down to the ground like a slide. Color the picture.

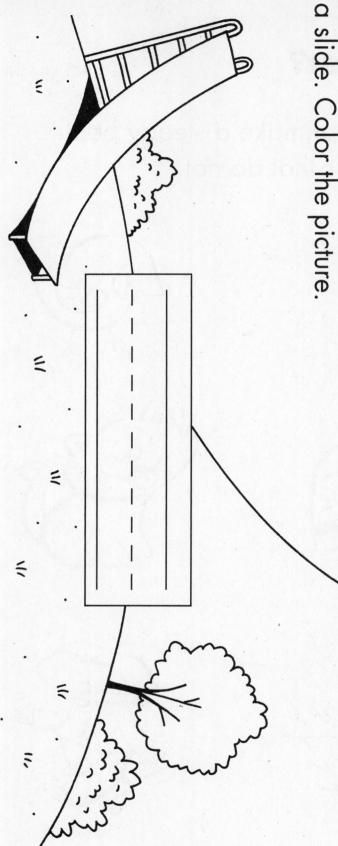

Rhythm Maze

Try to make each sound. Which two things make a steady beat? Color the footsteps that connect them.

Make Your Own Squiggle

Make sounds that match these squiggles as you trace them with your finger.

Make up your own squiggle, and draw it in these two boxes. Cut out the second box, and give your squiggle to a friend. Perform each other's squiggles!

Make a Poem Book

RESOURCE MASTER 1•8

Cut along the dotted lines. Then fold along the solid lines to make a book. Color the pictures. Draw yourself on the last page!

Rain on the hilltop,

Rain on the tree,

but not on me!

Rain on the green grass,

Your Musical Body

RESOURCE MASTER 1•9

  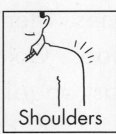  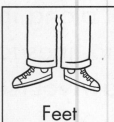

Fingers	Hands	Shoulders	Thighs	Feet

Snap!   Clap!   Tap!   Pat!   Stamp!

Draw a picture of yourself on the outline. When your teacher calls out a body part, point to it on the drawing and use that body part to make a sound.

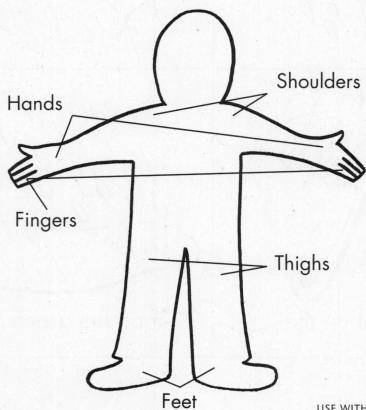

Write a Rhythm Piece

RESOURCE MASTER 1•10

Cut out the pieces at the bottom of the page. Arrange them in the boxes.

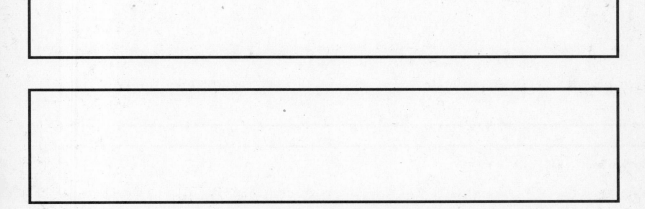

Have a friend perform your piece. Then mix up the pieces, and try again!

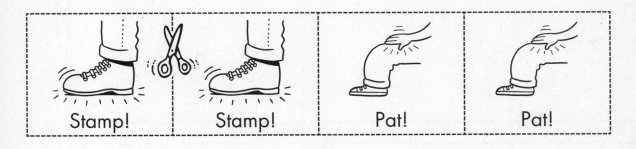

Stamp! | Stamp! | Pat! | Pat!

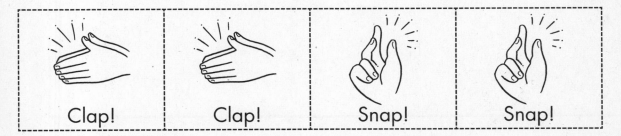

Clap! | Clap! | Snap! | Snap!

Squiggle Practice

RESOURCE MASTER 1•11

Listen to the music. If the music goes up, draw a squiggle up. If the music goes down, draw a squiggle down.

1.

2.

3.

4.

Spotlight Your Success! RESOURCE MASTER 1·12

Check Your Learning

1. Which has a steady beat?

a. clock

b. bird

2. Which has a sound that goes up and down?

a. bouncing ball

b. siren

Read and Listen

1. Listen to the music. Does the melody go up or down?

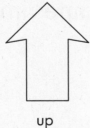

a. up

b. down

2. Listen to this song and pat the steady beat.

Spotlight Your Success! RESOURCE MASTER

Think!

1. Do you think a lullaby should have a steady beat or an unsteady beat? Why?

2. Why do you think sometimes music is soft and other music is loud?

3. Choose your favorite song from this unit and tell why you liked it.

Create and Perform

1. Create a movement that shows steady beat.

2. Add a movement that shows upward and downward sound.

3. Perform both movements at the same time.

Self-Assessment

Think about your project.
How did you do?
Put an X in the box.

	We sang at the right speed.	We moved with the beat.
😦		
😐		
🙂		
😁		

Teacher Assessment   RESOURCE MASTER

	Tempo	Movement
Excellent	Consistently sang with a steady tempo.	Moved with the steady beat throughout the entire performance.
***Competent**	Sang with a steady tempo most of the performance.	Moved with the steady beat almost all of the performance.
Progressing	Sang with a steady tempo some of the performance, but had occasional lapses.	Moved with the steady beat for part of the performance.
Showing Little Progress	Sang with an unsteady tempo most of the performance.	Moved with the steady beat very little of the performance.

Not Scorable: Did not participate.

***Competent is the expected level for all students.**

Name _____ Date _____

School-to-Home Letter

Dear Family,

The sounds of music are all around. Does your child enjoy imitating voices, tea kettles, and train engines; or does your child enjoy rhyming and singing? In this unit, children will learn to distinguish between long and short sounds in verse. They will learn to recognize the variation of these sounds in their environment— for example, the long sound of the train's *choo-choo* versus the short sound of fingers snapping.

Your child will also learn the difference between high and low sounds. For fun, we teach, "Touch your shoulders for higher sounds. Touch your waist when you hear lower sounds." Ask your child to demonstrate this while singing a favorite song. Your child will also learn to describe sounds and match them to pictures.

To learn about tone color, your child will perform different voice functions: speaking, singing, whispering, and calling. Ask your child to demonstrate these different voices. Toward the end of this unit, children will learn to identify solo and group or chorus patterns; and they will create an orchestra of animal sounds as we focus on melody.

Encourage your child to identify the different sounds heard at the playground, in your home, on the radio, or while shopping. Ask questions about the sounds, such as: "Is that sound long or short, loud or soft, high or low?" Help your child have fun as he or she explores the music and sounds around you!

Musically yours,

First Grade Music Teacher

School-to-Home Letter RESOURCE MASTER 2•1

Estimada Familia:

Los sonidos de la música están en todos lados. ¿Disfruta su hijo imitando voces, el sonido de las pavas o calderas y locomotoras, o disfruta haciendo rimas y cantando? En esta unidad, su hijo aprenderá a distinguir entre los sonidos largos y los sonidos cortos de un verso. Aprenderá a reconocer la variación de estos sonidos en su medio —por ejemplo, el sonido largo del *chu-chu* del tren en comparación con el sonido corto de los chasquidos de los dedos.

Su hijo también aprenderá las diferencias entre los sonidos agudos y graves. Para diversión les enseñamos, "Sonidos agudos, toca los hombros. Sonidos graves, toca la cintura". Pídale a su hijo que se lo demuestre mientras canta su canción favorita. Su hijo aprenderá a describir los sonidos y a vincular estos a dichos pies o entradas. Él o ella comenzarán a reconocer los tonos agudos o graves de instrumentos como la flauta y la tuba.

Para aprender sobre los colores del tono, su hijo realizará diferentes funciones de voz: hablar, cantar, susurrar y llamar en voz alta. Pídale a su hijo que le demuestre estas diferentes voces. Hacia el final de esta unidad, los niños aprenderán a identificar patrones de solos y grupales o de coro; y crearán una orquesta de sonidos de animales a medida que nos concentremos en la melodía.

Aliente a su hijo para que identifique los distintos sonidos que se escuchan en un patio de recreo, en su casa, en la radio o mientras está haciendo las compras. Haga preguntas sobre los sonidos, como por ejemplo: "¿El sonido es largo o corto, fuerte o suave, agudo o grave?" ¡Ayude a su hijo a divertirse mientras él o ella explora la música y los sonidos a su alrededor!

Atentamente,

Maestra de Música de Primer Grado

Creative Unit Project

RESOURCE MASTER

Help to make a "Sounds" book.
Follow these steps.

STEP 1
Look around.
What makes a long sound?
What makes a short sound?
Draw pictures. Cut them out for the book.

long

short

Creative Unit Project

RESOURCE MASTER 2·3

STEP 2

Look around.

What makes a high sound?

What makes a low sound?

Draw pictures. Cut them out for the book.

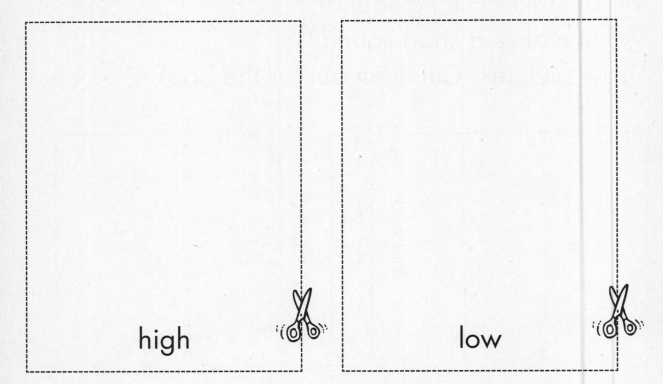

high   low

STEPS 3 and 4

Think about instruments. Think about their sounds.

What makes each type of sound?

long   short   high   low

Find pictures for the "Sounds" book.

Long or Short?

LONG sounds	SHORT sounds

Cut out the pictures. How does each thing sound? Paste the pictures in one of the boxes.

High or Low?

RESOURCE MASTER 2•5

Color the picture that makes a high sound in each box.

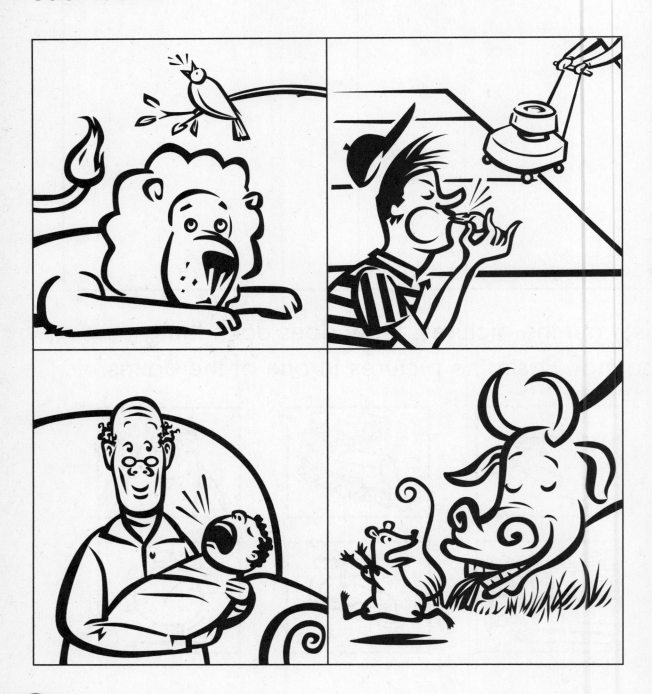

Arrows

Cut out the long and short arrows. Place the arrows next to their correct sounds in the book.

Flute and Tuba

Color the flute blue. Color the tuba orange.
Cut out the pictures.

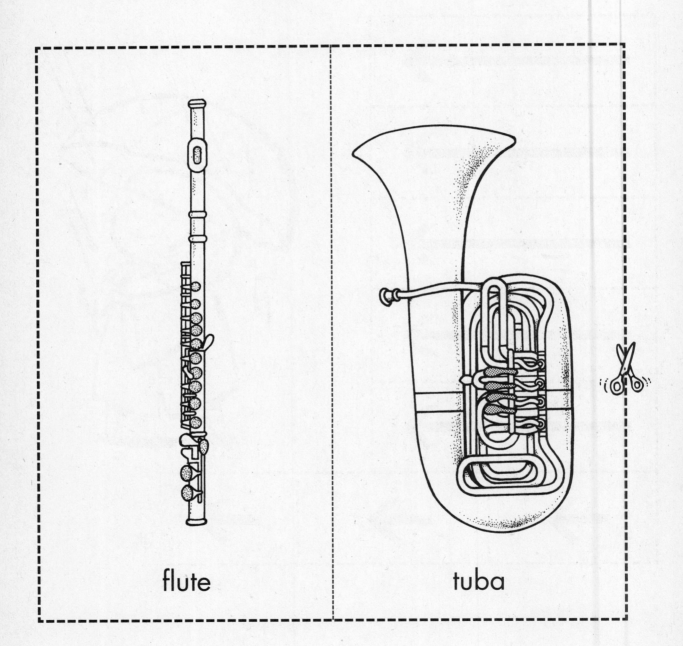

flute

tuba

Four Voices
Game Cards

Color and cut out the pictures.

WAIT!

Stick Puppets

RESOURCE MASTER 2•9

Color and cut out the pictures.
Paste each one on a stick to make puppets.

Animal Sound Symphony

 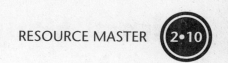

Color and cut out the cards.

Animal Sound Symphony

Color and cut out the cards.

Spotlight Your Success! RESOURCE MASTER 2•11

Check Your Learning

1. Which instrument makes a low sound?

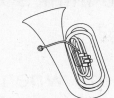

a. flute

b. tuba

2. Which word has a longer sound?

a. splash

b. pitter, patter

3. Which makes a shorter sound?

a. dog barking

b. airplane taking off

Read and Listen

1. Listen to the song. Raise your hand when you hear the longer sounds.

2. Listen to the song. Show "thumbs up" when you hear high sounds. Show "thumbs down" when you hear low sounds.

Spotlight Your Success! RESOURCE MASTER 2•11

Think!

1. Why do you think songs have both short and long sounds?

   Think of a time when you would use each voice.

singing	speaking
whispering	calling

2. Write your first name high on a page and make it look long. Then write your name low on the page and make it look short. Speak your name both ways.

Create and Perform

1. Create a rhythmic movement that shows either high-and-low or long-and-short.

2. Perform it for the class. Ask them to guess which one you are showing.

Self-Assessment

RESOURCE MASTER

Think about your project. How did you do? Put an X in the box.	I know long and short sounds.	I know high and low sounds.
😦		
😐		
🙂		
😁		

Teacher Assessment

RESOURCE MASTER 2•13

	Long and Short	High and Low
Excellent	Labeling of items in the book indicates a solid understanding of long and short sounds.	Labeling in the book shows a complete understanding of the concept high and low.
*Competent	Labeling of items in the book indicates a good understanding of long and short sounds.	Labeling in the book shows a substantial understanding of the concept high and low.
Progressing	Labeling of items in the book indicates a partial understanding of long and short sounds.	Labeling in the book shows a limited understanding of the concept high and low.
Showing Little Progress	Labeling of items in the book indicates a misunderstanding of long and short sounds.	Labeling in the book shows an incomplete understanding of the concept high and low.

Not Scorable: Did not participate.

*Competent is the expected level for all students.

School-to-Home Letter RESOURCE MASTER

Dear Family,

Rhythm and sound are important parts of your child's life. Children readily respond to the rhythms and sounds of the world around them. In this unit students will learn the difference between a steady beat and rhythm. Clapping, speaking, playing, and singing word rhythms will help your child master these concepts. Speak and clap familiar one-sound (syllable) and two-sound (syllable) words. Begin with things in your home such as *bed* (one sound) and *kitchen* (two sounds).

Your child will learn to identify the families of unpitched instruments and to describe the tone color of these instruments. Ask your child to describe the difference between the sounds of a drum and a triangle. Your child will also learn to read rhythmic notation and will perform easy rhythmic patterns using selected unpitched instruments.

Find items in and around your home that will produce found sound. A found sound is anything other than a conventional instrument that produces a sound. Can you and your child create rhythmic patterns using found sounds produced on pencils, spoons, rocks, or sticks? Then play some music. Lead your child to notice the rhythms of musical sounds and found sounds.

Continue exploring rhythm by reciting a favorite nursery rhyme. Clap the rhythm of the words as you say the rhyme. Have fun experiencing rhythm and sound with your child!

Sincerely,

First Grade Music Teacher

School-to-Home Letter RESOURCE MASTER

Estimada Familia:

El ritmo y el sonido son partes importantes en la vida de su hijo. Los niños responden con rapidez a los ritmos y a los sonidos del mundo que los rodea. En esta unidad los alumnos aprenderán la diferencia entre un compás y un ritmo continuo. Hacer palmas, decir, jugar y cantar rimas ayudará a su hijo a dominar estos conceptos. Diga y palmee palabras familiares de un sonido (sílaba) y de dos sonidos (silabas). Comience con objetos de su casa como por ejemplo *flor* (un sonido) y *cuarto* (dos sonidos).

Su hijo aprenderá a identificar las familias de instrumentos sin tono y a describir el color del tono de estos instrumentos. Pida a su hijo que describa las diferencias entre los sonidos de un tambor y los de un triángulo. Su hijo también aprenderá a leer la notación rítmica y ejecutará patrones o esquemas de ritmo fáciles utilizando instrumentos seleccionados sin tono.

Encuentre objetos en su casa que produzcan un 'sonido nuevo'. Un 'sonido nuevo' es cualquiera producido por algo que no sea un instrumento convencional para producir sonidos. ¿Pueden usted y su hijo crear esquemas rítmicos utilizando sonidos descubiertos producidos con lápices, cucharas, piedras o palos? Luego toquen alguna música. Guíe a su hijo para que tome conciencia de los ritmos de los sonidos musicales y de los descubiertos.

Continúe explorando el ritmo al recitar una canción de cuna favorita. Haga palmas al ritmo de las palabras mientras va diciendo la canción. ¡Diviértase experimentando el ritmo y el sonido con su hijo o hija!

Atentamente,

Maestra de Música de Primer Grado

Creative Unit Project

RESOURCE MASTER 3•2

Make up a rhythm.
Perform it with a poem.
Follow these steps.

STEP 1
Write a new word.
Match the number of sounds to the beat.

corn (1 sound) _____

critter (2 sounds) _____

Use your words in the poem.

STEP 2
Choose a word with 2 sounds.
Choose a word with 1 sound.
Cut them out.
Paste them on the beat bars.
Clap the rhythm.

Marco

ladies

dance

kick

bow

Creative Unit Project

STEP 3
Play "Double This."
Write the rhythm pattern. Use ♩ or ♫

Dou-ble	dou-ble	this	this

Dou-ble	dou-ble	that	that

Dou-ble	this	dou-ble	that

Dou-ble	dou-ble	this	that

STEP 4
Choose a line.
Practice. Then perform!

How Many Sounds?

RESOURCE MASTER

Say the name of each animal aloud.
Circle 1 if the name has one sound.
Circle 2 if the name has two sounds.

1 2	1 2	1 2
1 2	1 2	1 2

Finding the Family

Cut and paste each found sound below the correct instrument family.

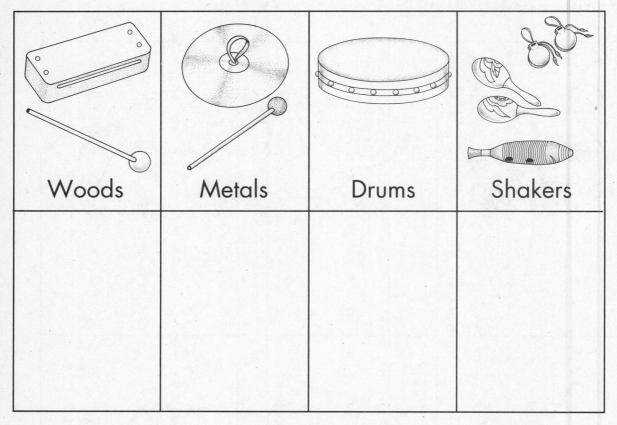

Woods	Metals	Drums	Shakers

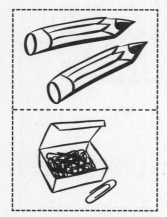
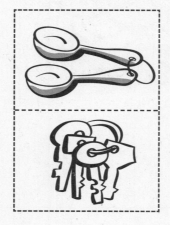

Playing Rhythms

♩ = 1 sound.

♫ = 2 sounds.

Clap or tap the beat.

Use

1

2

3

Name _____ Date _____

Singing Questions and Answers

Sing a question.
Your friend will sing the answer.

   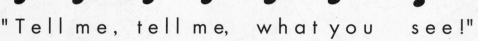
"Tell me, tell me, what you see!"

"You and me, that's what I see!"

"Tell me, tell me, what you hear!"

"Tell me, tell me, what you smell!"

40

Name _____ Date _____

Writing Rhythms

Trace the notes.

Quarter note	Eighth notes
	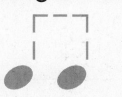

Use ♩ and
Write the rhythm on each beat bar.

Granny,   will your   dog   bite,

Cow   kick,   cat   scratch?

Granny,   will your   hen   peck?

"No,   child,   no."

Four-Beat Fun

RESOURCE MASTER 3•9

Color and cut out the pictures.
Arrange the pictures in a four-beat pattern.
Perform the pattern.

♩ Clap!

♫ Pat! Pat!

♫ Snap! Snap!

♩ Clap!

Create a Rhythm

RESOURCE MASTER 3•10

Trace the notes.

Quarter note	Eighth notes

Use ♩ and ♫

Write the rhythm on each beat bar.

Read the rhythm.

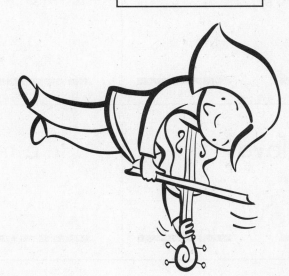

43

Think the Rhythm! Write It!

Write the rhythm above the beat bars.

Use ♩ and ♫

I like soda.	I like milk.
I like satin.	I like silk.
I like puppies.	I like kittens.
I like gloves.	I like mittens.

Spotlight Your Success! RESOURCE MASTER (3•12)

Check Your Learning

1. Which word has two sounds to the beat?

   a. corn

   b. crit-ter

2. Which one has a longer sound?

   a. ♩   b. ♫

Read and Listen

1. Listen to this song and pat the steady beat.

2. Listen to the same song and clap the rhythm.

3. Read these two rhythms.

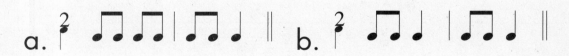

   Then listen to the music. Which rhythm pattern do you hear?

Spotlight Your Success! RESOURCE MASTER

Think!

1. How would you change the name Jim to fit two sounds to a beat?

2. Which goes with the words of a song— steady beat or rhythm?

3. Why do composers use notes to write their music?

Create and Perform

1. Create a rhythm pattern that lasts for four beats. Use one and two sounds to a beat.

2. Add words to your rhythm pattern.

_____ _____

3. Play your rhythm.
   Choose an instrument.

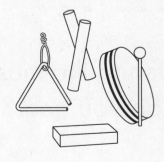

Self-Assessment

RESOURCE MASTER

Think about your project.
How did you do?
Put an X in the box.

	We played the rhythm well.	We played with a steady beat.	We stayed together.
😐			
🙂			
😊			
😁			

Teacher Assessment

RESOURCE MASTER 3•14

	Rhythm	Tempo	Played Together
Excellent	Played the rhythm accurately.	Consistently played with a steady tempo.	Played together as an ensemble with no teacher assistance.
*Competent	Played the rhythm with few mistakes.	Played with a steady tempo most of the performance.	Played together as an ensemble with minimal teacher assistance.
Progressing	Played the rhythm with several mistakes.	Played with steady tempo some of the performance, but had occasional lapses.	Played together as an ensemble with moderate teacher assistance.
Showing Little Progress	Played the rhythm with many mistakes.	Played with an unsteady tempo most of the performance	Played together as an ensemble with considerable teacher assistance.

Not Scorable: Did not participate.

*Competent is the expected level for all students.

School-to-Home Letter

RESOURCE MASTER 4•1

Dear Family,

Differences in pitch and rhythm form the foundations of music. In this unit your child will learn to hear these relationships as the class listens to musical examples from around the world. The class will explore these concepts by asking the following questions: Is one pitch higher or lower than another? Is the tempo of a piece steady, or does it get faster or slower? Does a large instrument like a cello make a higher or lower sound than a small instrument like a violin?

Your child will practice hearing, singing, and writing the pitches *mi* and *so,* the third and fifth notes in the scale. *Peter and the Wolf* by Sergei Prokofiev will introduce your child to musical themes and help him or her recognize the sounds of different instruments.

As always, you can enhance these lessons by taking time to listen to music with your child. As you listen to a piece, ask whether the tempo is fast or slow. Does it change? Pat out the beat together to find out. See what instruments you can hear in an orchestral piece. Encourage your child to talk about the way a certain piece of music makes him or her feel. Practice singing *so* and *mi* as you do the hand signals for each note. If you do not know the hand signals, your child should be happy to teach you!

Sincerely,

First Grade Music Teacher

School-to-Home Letter RESOURCE MASTER

Estimada Familia:

Las diferencias en tono y ritmo conforman los cimientos de la música. En esta unidad su hijo aprenderá a escuchar esas relaciones mientras la clase escucha muestras de músicas de todo el mundo. La clase explorará estos conceptos formulando las siguientes preguntas: ¿Es un tono más agudo o más grave que otro? ¿Es el tempo de una pieza continuo, o se acelera o desacelera? ¿Un instrumento grande como el chelo produce un sonido más agudo o más grave que un instrumento pequeño como el violín?

Su hijo practicará escuchando, cantando y escribiendo los tonos *mi y sol,* que son la tercera y la quinta nota de la escala. *Peter and the Wolf* de Sergei Prokofiev presentará a su hijo los temas musicales y lo ayudará a reconocer los sonidos de diferentes instrumentos.

Como siempre, usted puede mejorar estas lecciones tomándose el tiempo para escuchar música con su hijo. Mientras escuchan una pieza, pregúntele si el tempo es rápido o lento. ¿Cambia? Siga el compás tamborileando juntos para descubrirlo. Vean qué instrumentos pueden escuchar en una pieza orquestal. Aliente a su hijo para que hable sobre el modo en que una determinada pieza de música lo hace sentir. Practique cantando sol y mi mientras hace los símbolos con la mano para cada nota. Si no conoce los símbolos de las manos, ¡seguro su hijo o hija se alegrará de enseñárselos!

Atentamente,

Maestra de Música de Primer Grado

Creative Unit Project

RESOURCE MASTER 4•2

Write a song for "One, Two, Three, Four."
Perform it.
Follow these steps.

STEP 1
Read the poem.
Now sing it. Go high or low.

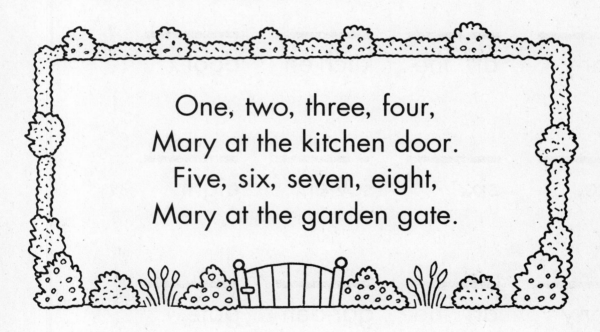

One, two, three, four,
Mary at the kitchen door.
Five, six, seven, eight,
Mary at the garden gate.

STEP 2
Read the poem.
Go faster or slower.
Now practice going slow. Keep a steady beat.

Creative Unit Project

RESOURCE MASTER

STEP 3

Write the rhythm of the poem. Use ♩ and ♫

One, two, three, four,

Mar-y at the kitch-en door.

Five, six, sev-en, eight,

Mar-y at the gar-den gate.

STEP 4

Write a *so-mi* melody for the poem. Use Resource Master 4-8. Practice singing the song. Then perform!

Name _____ Date _____

High or Low?

Write H under instruments that make a high sound.
Write L under instruments that make a low sound.

H _____	L _____
_____	_____
_____	_____
_____	_____

Fast or Slow?

RESOURCE MASTER 4•5

Make puppets.
Color and cut out the pictures.
Tape the pictures on sticks.

Name _____ Date _____

Lines and Spaces

Notes on lines look like this:

Notes in spaces look like this:

Cut out the notes. Place the notes on lines and in spaces on the staff. Draw a stem on each note.

Writing *So* and *Mi*

RESOURCE MASTER 4•7

When *so* is on a line, *mi* is on the line below.
Trace *so* and *mi* on the staff.

so　　　mi　　　so　　　mi

When *so* is on a space, *mi* is on the space below.
Trace *so* and *mi* on the staff.

so　　　mi　　　so　　　mi

Write a *So-Mi* Melody

RESOURCE MASTER

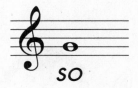
so

mi

Clap the rhythm of each line. Write the note *so* or *mi* above each syllable. Draw a stem on each note. Sing your new song.

One,   two,   three,   four,

Mar - y   at   the   kitch - en   door.

Five,   six   sev - en, eight,

Mar - y   at   the   gar - den   gate.

Name _____ Date _____

Peter and the Wolf Puppets

Make puppets.
Color and cut out the pictures.
Tape them to sticks.

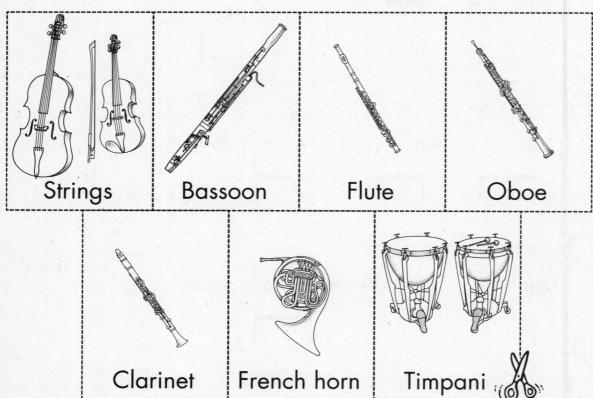

Strings

Bassoon

Flute

Oboe

Clarinet

French horn

Timpani

Peter and the Wolf Puppets

Make puppets.

Color and cut out the pictures.

Tape them to sticks.

Grandfather | Peter | Bird | Duck

Cat | Wolf | Hunters

A Musical Picture

RESOURCE MASTER

Listen to "The Green Grass Grows All Around."
Draw a picture to show how the music makes you feel.

Spotlight Your Success! RESOURCE MASTER

Check Your Learning

1. This 🎼 is called a

   a. pitch   b. staff   c. beat

2. These 𝄆   𝄇 tell you to

   a. start over at the beginning

   b. go to the end of the song

   c. repeat everything inside them

Read and Listen

1. Listen to the same song twice. Which one was slower?

   a. first one   b. second one

2. Listen to two different melodies. Which one has only so mi?

   a. first one   b. second one

Spotlight Your Success! RESOURCE MASTER 4•11

Think!

1. Why does some music go fast and some music go slow?

2. There is a different instrument for each character in "Peter and the Wolf." Do you think that is a good idea? Why or why not?

3. Which song in this unit did you like best? Why?

Create and Perform

1. Create a four-beat rhythm pattern using one and two sounds a beat.

_____ _____ _____ _____

2. Play your rhythm pattern with the pitches so and mi.

3. Add words to your melody and sing it for the class.

Self-Assessment

RESOURCE MASTER

		We wrote the *so, mi* notes correctly.	We played fast or slow at the right times.	We played loud or soft at the right times.	We all took part in the project.
Think about your project. How did you do? Put an X in the box.	😐				
	🙂				
	😊				
	😁				

Teacher Assessment

RESOURCE MASTER 4•13

	Notation	Tempo and Dynamics	Group Participation
Excellent	Notated the *so-mi* melody with no mistakes.	Performed chosen tempo and dynamic markings accurately throughout the performance.	All of the children participated in creating and performing in a group with enthusiasm.
*Competent	Notated the *so-mi* melody with few mistakes.	Performed chosen tempo and dynamic markings accurately through almost all of the performance.	Almost all of the children participated in creating and performing in a group with enthusiasm.
Progressing	Notated the *so-mi* melody with several mistakes.	Performed chosen tempo and dynamic markings accurately through some of the performance.	Some of the children participated in creating and performing in a group with enthusiasm.
Showing Little Progress	Notated the *so-mi* melody with many mistakes.	Performed chosen tempo and dynamic markings accurately very little during the performance.	Very few of the children participated in creating and performing in a group with enthusiasm.

Not Scorable: Did not participate.

*Competent is the expected level for all students.

USE WITH GRADE 1, UNIT 4, CREATIVE UNIT PROJECT

School-to-Home Letter

RESOURCE MASTER 5•1

Dear Family,

Have you ever noticed that silence is also a part of music? The next time you listen to a song, pay attention to the silent parts of the song as well as to the sounds. Help your child realize that without silence, the musical notes would simply run together as noise.

In this unit your child will continue to build his or her musical knowledge. Your child will learn to recognize picture patterns to show two beats, one beat, and no beat. The class will explore melody through word and voice. Your child will learn pitch through placement relationships on the body. Ask him or her to identify where *mi, so,* and *la* are on the body. (The waist level is *mi*; the chest level is *so*; and the mouth level is *la*.) Ask your child to demonstrate singing the sound at each level. Then help your child practice singing different combinations of *mi, so,* and *la*.

Your child will begin to perform rhythmic patterns alone, with others, and on instruments. By the end of the unit, your child will read, create, and even improvise musical patterns. This is no small feat for a child. A Zimbabwean proverb says, "If you can walk, you can dance. If you can talk, you can sing." Encourage your child to dance and sing—it makes living a lot more fun!

Sincerely,

First Grade Music Teacher

School-to-Home Letter

RESOURCE MASTER 5•1

Estimada Familia:

¿Alguna vez se ha percatado de que el silencio también es parte de la música? La próxima vez que escuche una canción, preste atención a los silencios de la canción y también a los sonidos. Ayude a su hijo a entender que sin silencio, las notas musicales solamente correrían juntas como ruido.

En esta unidad su hijo continuará construyendo su conocimiento musical. Su hijo aprenderá a reconocer esquemas de patrones pictóricos para indicar dos compases, un compás y ausencia de compases. La clase explorará la melodía mediante la palabra y la voz. Su hijo aprenderá el tono mediante relaciones de ubicación en el cuerpo. Pídale que identifique dónde se encuentran *mi, sol,* y *la* en el cuerpo. (El nivel de la cintura es mi, el nivel del pecho es sol y el nivel de la boca es la.) Pídale a su hijo que lo demuestre cantando los sonidos de cada nivel. Luego ayude a su hijo a practicar cantando diferentes combinaciones de *mi, sol* y *la.*

Su hijo comenzará a ejecutar esquemas rítmicos solo, con otros niños y con instrumentos. Hacia el final de la unidad, su hijo leerá, creará, e inclusive improvisará esquemas musicales. No es tarea fácil para un niño. Un proverbio de Zimbawe dice "Si puedes caminar, puedes bailar. Si puedes hablar, puedes cantar". Aliente a su hijo o hija para que baile y cantee. ¡La vida se vuelve mucho más divertida!

Atentamente,

Maestra de Música de Primer Grado

Creative Unit Project

Mi is here.

So is here.

The new pitch is here.

Write a pattern with these notes.

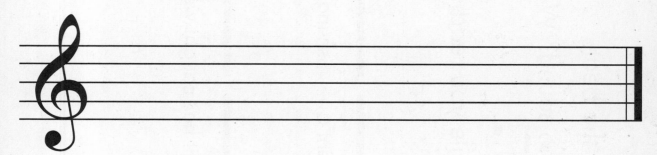

Practice your music. Then perform!

Creative Unit Project

Read the poem. Pat the beat.

Which beats have no sound? Write a ξ.

Now write ♩ and ♫

Clap the rhythm while you read.

Sim-ple	Si-mon	went a	fish-ing	for to	catch a	whale.

All the	fish - es	that he	caught were	in his	moth - er's	pail.

One or Two Beats

RESOURCE MASTER 5•4

Color and cut out the pictures.
Make a picture beat pattern.
Paste two boats above the bar for two sounds.
Paste one boat above the bar for one sound.
Paste no picture for no sound.

Clap your beat pattern for a friend.

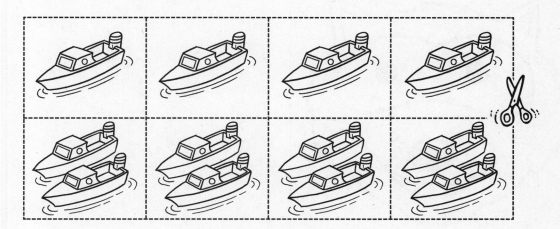

Kobuta Puppets

RESOURCE MASTER 5•5

Make puppets.
Color and cut out the pictures. Fold.
Paste on a stick.

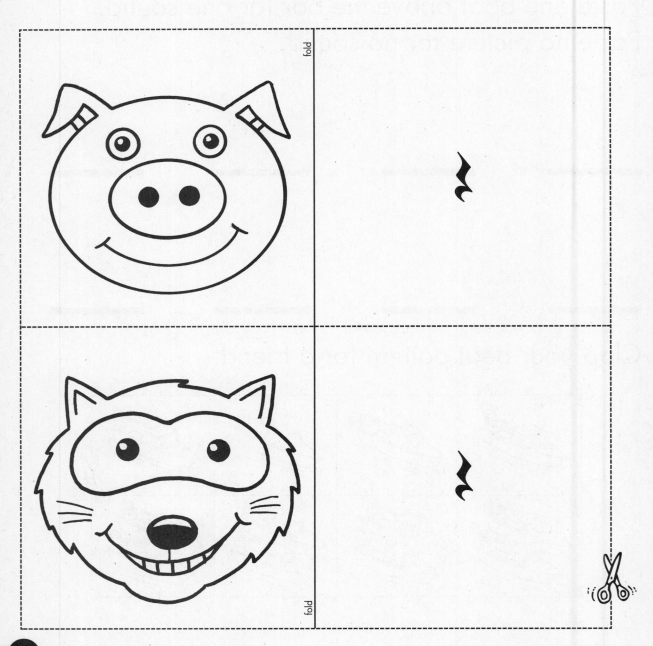

Kobuta Puppets

Make more puppets.

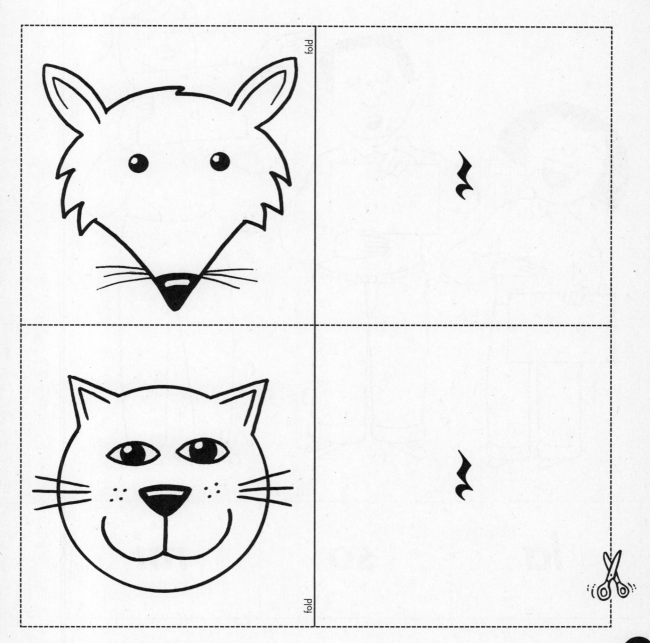

fold

fold

Mi, So, and *La*

Which sound is each child singing? Cut and paste *mi, so,* and *la* to go with the correct child.

la	so	mi

Word Beats

Say each word.
Circle the number of beats in each word.

table	elephant	computer
2 3	2 3	2 3
telephone	baby	salad
2 3	2 3	2 3

Name _____ Date _____

Pitty Patty Polt

Read and clap each pattern.

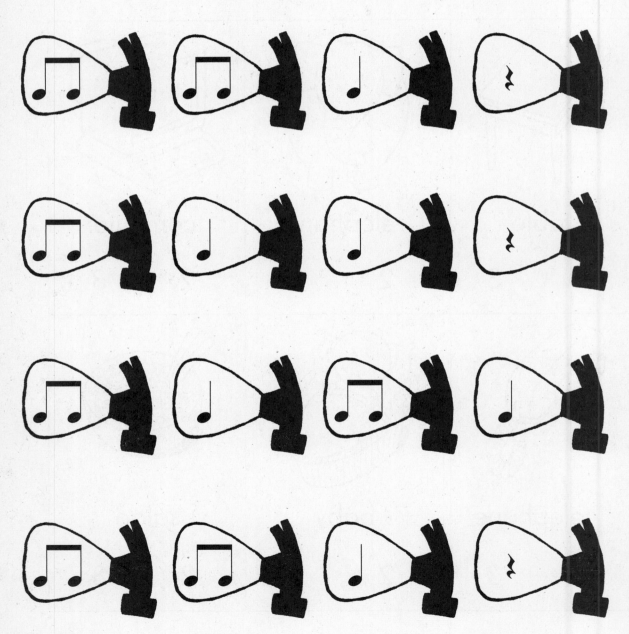

Pitty Patty Polt

RESOURCE MASTER 5•8

Read and clap the pattern.
Write ♫ ♩ or 𝄽 to show
the pattern.

Pitty	Patty	Polt	
▬	▬	▬	▬
Shoe the	black	colt	
▬	▬	▬	▬
Here a	nail,	there a	nail
▬	▬	▬	▬
Pitty	Patty	Polt	
▬	▬	▬	▬

Each box is a beat. Make your own rhythm.
Write ♫ ♩ or 𝄽 in each box.
Read and clap each pattern.

Mi, So, La Melodies

Point to the notes as you sing.
Sing *mi-so-la.*
Sing *la-so-mi.*
Sing *so-la-mi.*

mi   so   la

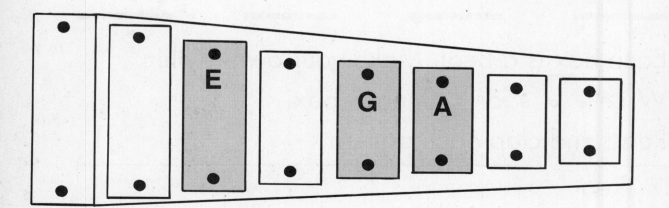

Spotlight Your Success! RESOURCE MASTER (5•10)

Review

1. A 𝄽 means
   a. three sounds to a beat
   b. two sounds to a beat
   c. no sound to a beat

2. Here are so and mi. Which note is la?
   a.   b.

3. Here are so and mi. Which note is la?
   a.   b.

Read and Listen

1. Read these rhythm patterns.
   Then listen. Which one do you hear?

   a.   b.

2. Reach these pitches. **Tinker, Tailor**
   Then listen. Which melody uses so la?

   a.   b.

Spotlight Your Success! RESOURCE MASTER 5•10

Think!

1. How are a quarter note and a quarter rest different?

2. Why do you think some beats have no sound?

3. Why do you think some games have songs?

Create and Perform

1. Create your own four-beat melody. Use so, mi, and la.

_____ _____ _____ _____

2. Start with one sound to a beat.

3. Change some sounds to two sounds to a beat.

4. Then sing your melody with the syllables.

mi   *so*   *la*

E   G   A

Self-Assessment

Think about your project.
How did you do?
Put an X in the box.

Our sounds worked out well.

We worked well together.

We had fun doing our performance.

Teacher Assessment

RESOURCE MASTER 5•12

	"Sound Pictures"	Group Work	Focus and Confidence
Excellent	The "sound pictures" depicted the characters and actions well throughout the performance and enhanced the story.	The children worked together cooperatively with no difficulty.	Consistently, the group performed with excellent focus and engaging confidence.
*Competent	The "sound pictures" depicted the characters and actions well through most of the performance.	The children worked together cooperatively with little difficulty.	Generally, the group performed with focus and confidence.
Progressing	The "sound pictures" depicted the characters and actions well through some of the performance.	The children worked together cooperatively with occasional difficulty.	Sporadically, the group performed with focus and confidence.
Showing Little Progress	The "sound pictures" depicted the characters and actions during very little of the performance and, at times, detracted from the story.	The children worked together cooperatively with a lot of difficulty.	Occasionally, the group performed with focus and confidence.

Not Scorable: Did not participate.

*Competent is the expected level for all students.

School-to-Home Letter

RESOURCE MASTER 6•1

Dear Family,

Music is made up of different sections. When the sections are combined, the result is a whole song. In this last unit of our music curriculum, your child will sing, play, move, analyze, and listen to gain a better understanding of A B and A B A forms in music. In A B form, the A section opens the song and alternates with the B section. In A B A form, the A section opens the song, the B section follows, and then the A section is repeated.

Using the notes *mi, so,* and *la,* your child will create a two-part song (A B form). Many familiar songs are written in A B form with a verse followed by a chorus. "Oh, Susanna" is an example of a song written in A B form. Listen to songs with your child, and help him or her identify songs with two parts.

Every voice, like every instrument, has its own sound or characteristics (tone color). By singing, speaking, calling, and whispering, your child will experience and learn to identify different vocal tone colors. When you are talking with your child, use your voice in different ways and ask him or her to describe the tone color of the voice you are using.

In this unit your child will also sing and listen to music from other countries. He or she will be introduced to a Chinese "fiddle" known as an erhu. This instrument is very popular with schoolchildren in China and is used in orchestral music as well as to accompany folk music.

Encourage your child to share the new songs he or she learns to sing at school. Sharing music is fun!

Sincerely,

First Grade Music Teacher

School-to-Home Letter RESOURCE MASTER

Estimada Familia:

La música está compuesta de diferentes secciones. Cuando las secciones se combinan, el resultado es una canción completa. En esta última unidad de nuestro programa musical, su hijo cantará, tocará, se moverá, analizará y escuchará para comprender mejor los esquemas musicales A B y A B A. En el esquema A B, la sección A abre la canción y alterna con la sección B. En un esquema A B A, la sección A abre la canción, la sección B le sigue y luego se repite la sección A.

Usando las notas *mi, sol* y *la,* su hijo creará una canción compuesta por dos partes (esquema A B). Muchas canciones conocidas están escritas en esquema A B con el verso seguido por un coro. "*Oh, Susanna*" es un ejemplo de una canción escrita en esquema A B. Escuche canciones con su hijo y ayúdelo a identificar las que tengan dos partes.

Cada voz, al igual que cada instrumento, tiene sus propios sonidos o características (color del tono). Al cantar, pronunciar, decir en voz alta y murmurar, su hijo experimentará y aprenderá a identificar diferentes colores de los tonos vocales. Cuando hable con su hijo, utilice su voz de diferentes modos y pídale que describa el color del tono de la voz que usted está usando.

En esta unidad su hijo también cantará y escuchará música de otros países. Conocerán un "violín" chino conocido como erhu. Este instrumento es muy popular entre los alumnos de China y se usa en la música orquestal y también para acompañar música *folk*.

Aliente a su hijo o hija a que comparta las nuevas canciones que aprende a cantar en la escuela. ¡Compartir música es algo realmente divertido!

Atentamente,

Maestra de Música de Primer Grado

Creative Unit Project

RESOURCE MASTER

Work with your partner.
Make up a word pattern.
Make up a rhythm and melody to match.

STEP 1
Think of words about:

- Elephants   • Spiders   • Spider webs

Write the words.

_____

_____

Make up a four-beat pattern. Match the words.

Use ♩, ♫, 𝄽
Write the pattern over the beat bars.
Write the words under the beat bars.

▬▬ ▬▬ ▬ ▬

Creative Unit Project

RESOURCE MASTER 6•3

STEP 2

Look at your rhythm pattern.
Write a melody to go with it.
Use *mi, so, la*.

Write the notes.

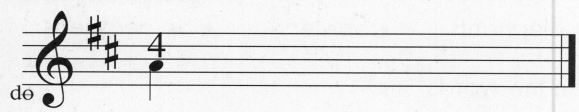

Practice your melody.
Then join another pair of students.
Play your melodies together.
Use AB or ABA form.

STEP 3

Put together your 4-beat melodies. Now you have 8 beats.
Make a piece with "One Little Elephant." It is the A section. Your 8-beat melody is the B section.

STEP 4

Perform!

Choose Part "A"

Create a two-part song. Sing each melody.
Circle the one you like best.

1.

mi   so   la

I have   rhy-thm like   this.

2.

mi   so   la

I have   rhy-thm like   this.

Write Part "B"

Complete the two-part song.

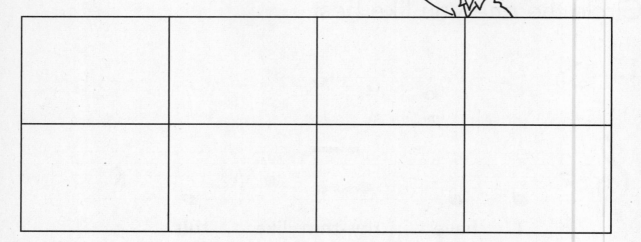

Select notes and rests.
Cut and paste the notes and rests into the boxes.

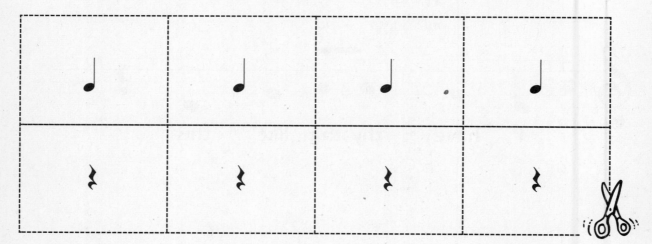

Sing and clap to perform your song.
Use this page and page 85.

Name _____ Date _____

One Little Elephant

Create a rhythm and speech section
for the song "One Little Elephant."
Write notes and rests above the beat bars.
Write four-beat word rhythms below the beat bars.
Sing the new song.

Write a Melody

Pick *mi*, *so*, or *la*. Fill in the
notes in any order you like.

mi   so   la

Pit   pat   well - a - day,

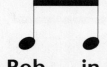

Lit - tle   Rob - in   flew   a - way.

Where can   Lit - tle   Rob - in   be?

Gone in - to   the   cher - ry   tree.

The Chinese Erhu

The erhu (AIR-hoo) is an important instrument in China. The bottom part is made of wood. It looks like a small drum. One end is covered with snakeskin. The other end is open. The erhu has a long, thin neck. To make a sound, the player touches the strings while moving the bow.

Erhu
Chinese "fiddle"

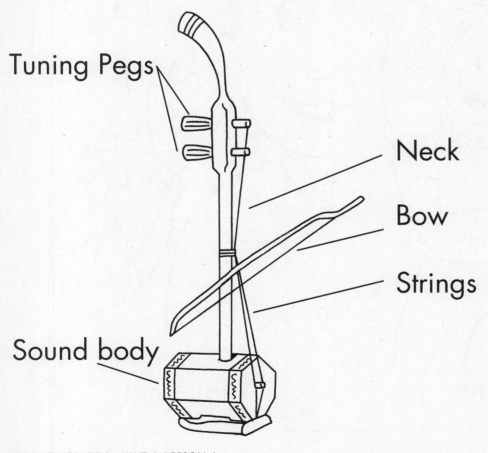

Tuning Pegs

Neck

Bow

Strings

Sound body

Using Your Voice

Make puppets.
Color and cut out the pictures.
Paste each one on a stick.

Singing

Whispering

Name _____ Date _____

Using Your Voice

Make more puppets.

Speaking

Calling

Hello!

Best Friends

RESOURCE MASTER

Draw a picture of your best friend.

Spotlight Your Success! RESOURCE MASTER (6•11)

Review

1. Music that has two parts is called:

   a. *so la*　　　　b. AB　　　　c. ABA

2. Here are *so* and *mi*. 🎼 Where is *la*?

   a. on the first space

   b. on the second space

   c. on the third space

Read and Listen

1. Read these rhythms. Then listen. Which melody do you hear?

   a. 🎵　　　　b. 🎵

2. Read these pitches. 🎼
   Then listen. Which melody do you hear?

   a. 🎼　　　　b. 🎼

Spotlight Your Success! RESOURCE MASTER 6•11

Think!

1. How is a drum like a xylophone?

2. Which do you like better—singing songs or playing instruments? Why?

3. What is your favorite song? What do you like about it?

Create and Perform

1. Create an eight-beat rhythm pattern using one and two sounds a beat ending with a rest.

   _____ _____ _____ _____ |

   _____ _____ _____ _____ ‖

2. Play your rhythm pattern with the pitches so, mi and la on a pitched instrument.

3. Combine your melody with a partner's and play both melodies as an AB form.

94

Self-Assessment

RESOURCE MASTER

Think about your project.
How did you do?
Put an X in the box.

	Our rhythm matched the words.	We wrote our notes correctly and clearly.	We stayed together.
😕			
🙂			
😊			
😃			

Name _____ Date _____

Teacher Assessment

RESOURCE MASTER 6•13

	Rhythm to Words	Notation	Ensemble
Excellent	Matched the rhythm to the words accurately.	Notation was correct, neat, and very readable.	Performed together as an ensemble with no difficulty.
***Competent**	Matched the rhythm to the words almost accurately.	Almost all of the notation was correct, neat, and readable.	Performed together as an ensemble with little difficulty.
Progressing	Matched the rhythm to some of the words accurately.	Most of the notation was correct and readable, but some symbols were unclear, incorrect, and/or difficult to read.	Performed as an ensemble with some difficulty staying together.
Showing Little Progress	Matched the rhythm to a few of the words accurately.	Notation was generally difficult to read, with many symbols being unclear or incorrect.	Performed as an ensemble with a great deal of difficulty staying together.

Not Scorable: Did not participate.

*Competent is the expected level for all students.

USE WITH GRADE 1, UNIT 6, CREATIVE UNIT PROJECT

Welcome to Music Class!

Circle all of your favorite things to do in music class.

Singing

Playing Instruments

Moving

Writing Music Notes

Performing

Playing Games

Making Up Songs

Listening to Music

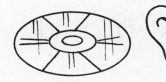

Upward and Downward

Look at these two keyboards. Circle the keyboard that shows the arrow going upward.

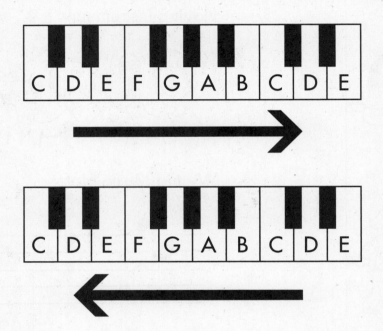

Choose upward or downward sounds. Write three words from the poem "Night Comes." Add the words to your upward or downward sounds.

_____

_____

Play your upward or downward sounds with the poem.

Connect the Dots

RESOURCE MASTER R•3

Connect the dots below:

Oh, the wind blew East (make wind sound)

. . . . . >
1 2 3 4 5 6

Oh, the wind blew West (make wind sound)

< . . . . .
6 5 4 3 2 1

The wind blew the Sunshine right down to town

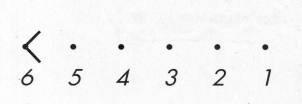

. . . . . .
1 . 3 . 5 . 7 . 9 . 11
  2   4   6   8   10

Hunt the Cows

Sing the song. Point to the long and short sounds.

The   sun   is   hot, _____

The   cows   are   lost, _____

I   think   I'll   rest, _____

'Till   they   come   home. _____

Longer-Shorter Notes

RESOURCE MASTER R•5

Sing the second verse of "This Little Light of Mine." Follow the pictures.

Ev–	'ry–	where	I	go,
I'm	gon– na let		it	shine,
Ev–	'ry–	where	I	go,
I'm	gon– na let		it	shine,
Ev–	'ry–	where	I	go,
I'm	gon– na let		it	shine,
Let	it	shine,		
Let	it	shine,		
Let	it	shine.		

Composing a Melody with Higher/Lower

RESOURCE MASTER

1. Look at these bars.

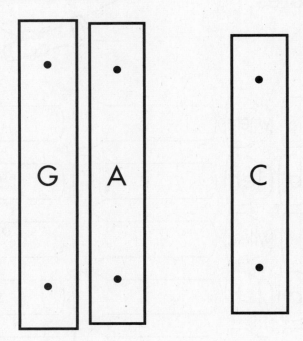

2. Play the three pitches in any order you like.

3. Create a melody. Play your pitches again four times. End with C.

4. Play your melody again. Listen for the higher and lower sounds.

Snails Get Moving

RESOURCE MASTER (R•7)

Some songs have one or two sounds per beat.
Use the snails to practice one and two beats.

Notes to the teacher: Copy and cut out five of the one-sound-per-beat squares. Copy and cut out three two-sound-per-beat squares. Arrange them in the correct order on the floor. Have children step on the correct squares as they wind around in a circle.

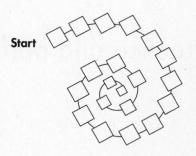

Start

103

Quarter Notes and Eighth-Note Pairs

RESOURCE MASTER R•8

Listen to two rhythms. Circle the rhythm you hear.

a. ♩ ♫ ♫ ♩   b. ♩ ♩ ♫ ♩

Copy the rhythm you heard in the box.

Form groups. Make up your own music about a wagon passing by.

1. Use the rhythm in the box above.

2. Choose instruments for your music.

3. Draw a picture of what you think the wagon looks like.

4. Practice and perform your music for the class.

Name That Tune

RESOURCE MASTER

Draw lines to connect the *so-mi* melody with the correct song.

1. 2, 4, 6, 8

2. Seesaw

3. Bee, Bee, Bumblebee

4. Here We Sit

Which two songs have exactly the same melody? Circle the numbers of the correct songs.

1   2   3   4

A *Mi-So* Melody for "Wings"

RESOURCE MASTER R•10

Write a *mi-so* melody for the poem "Wings."

Mi will be on the first line.
So will be on the second line.

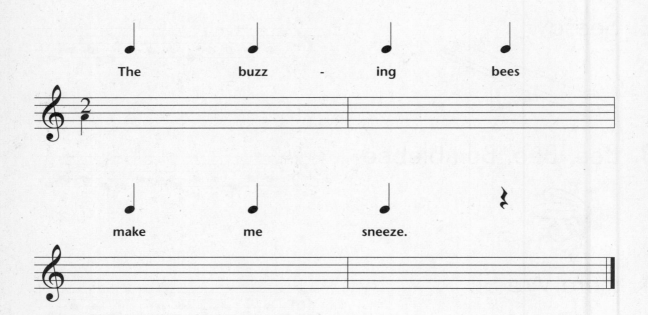

The buzz - ing bees

make me sneeze.

Play your melody.

Make a Song Map

Look at the *mi-so* song map.

1. Here   we   sit   in   a   ring.

so – so   so – so
              mi   mi

2. Close your eyes   now while   we   sing.

so – so   so – so
          mi – mi   mi

Now you try it.

1. Here   we   sit   in   a   ring.

2. Close your eyes   now while   we   sing.

Here We Sit

RESOURCE MASTER

Which phrase starts on *mi*? Circle your answer.

1   2   3   4

1. so / mi

2. so / mi

3. so / mi

4. so / mi

Teacher's Note: Ask children to sing each puzzle piece using *so* and *mi*. Then have them cut out the pieces and arrange them in a new order. Ask children to sing them using so and mi in the new order. Finally, have children put them back in the original order.

Where Is *La*?

Look at the music. Fill in the blanks with *mi, so,* and *la.* The first one is done for you.

so ___ ___ ___

___ ___ ___ ___ ___ ___ ___

Sing the pitch names. What song is it?

_____

Sing a Story

RESOURCE MASTER R•14

Sing "Lucy Locket." Put the pictures in order.
Write the number under the picture.

1 _____   _____

_____   _____

Quarter Rest

What makes me happy?
What makes me sad?

Clap this rhythm pattern.

What   makes   me   hap-py?

Is there a silent beat at the end of the pattern?
Circle your answer.   **Yes   No**

Clap this rhythm pattern.

What   makes   me   sad.

Is there a silent beat at the end of the pattern?
Circle your answer.   **Yes   No**

Silent Beat ⁋

1. Trace the quarter rest.

2. Practice drawing rests.

_____ _____ _____ _____

3. Fill in the silent beat quarter rest in the song.

Pease   porridge   hot   _____

Pease   porridge   cold   _____

Pease   porridge   in   the   pot

Nine   days   old   _____

Composing Rhythms

Choose a one-beat symbol to fill in each square.

Teacher: Have children play ♩ on drums and ♫ on woodblocks, and have them say "Psssh" for the 𝄽.

Teacher: Have children play ♩ on cymbals and ♫ on sticks, and have them say "Psssh" for the 𝄽.

Teacher: Have children decide what instrument to play.

Finding *La*

Star Light, Star Bright

Traditional

Star - light, star bright,

First star I see to - night,

I wish I may, I wish I might,

Have the wish I wish to - night.

Teacher: Ask children to sing the song with the words. Then ask them to sing the song again with *so* and *mi*. Have them circle the odd note and sing it again with *so, mi,* and *la.*

Tracing *So, Mi, La*

Trace the notes. Fill in the blanks with the correct pitch syllables.

1.

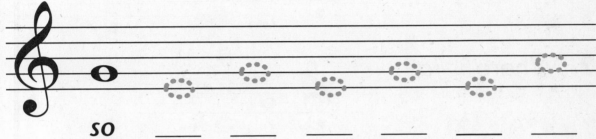

so   ___ ___ ___ ___ ___

2.

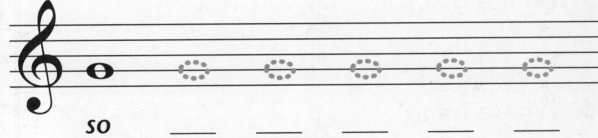

so   ___ ___ ___ ___ ___

Which song is "Star Light, Star Bright?"

Circle your answer.   **1   2**

Draw *So*, *Mi*, and *La*

RESOURCE MASTER R•20

Draw the missing notes on the staff.

1. Where is *mi*?

la

2. Where is *la*?

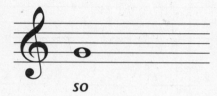

so

3. Where is *so*?

mi

4. Where is *mi*?

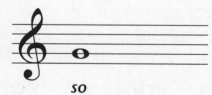

so

5. Where is *la*?

mi

6. Where is *so*?

la

Match the Rhythm

RESOURCE MASTER

Draw a line from the picture to the rhythm of the song.

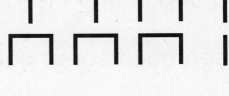

"Lucy Locket"

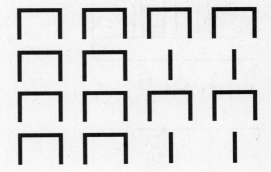

"Seesaw"

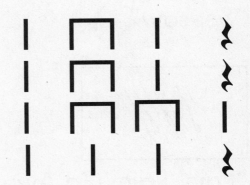

"Snail, Snail"

"Pease Porridge Hot"

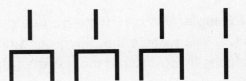

117

Perform a Concert

Sing the songs in order.
Play along, using the C and G bells.

Between each song, count 8 beats on the bells.

1.

2, 4, 6, 8

2.

"Here We Sit"

3.

"Seesaw"

4.

"Bee, Bee, Bumblebee"

5.

"Rain, Rain, Go Away"

6.

"Pease Porridge Hot"

Teacher: Narrate the "Song Story" below by developing a storyline using the "characters" in the songs, or have the children help make up their own story.

Story Example: We met at the garden gate (1). Then we sat in a circle and talked (2). We went to the playground and played on the seesaw (3). There were bumblebees flying around the flowers (4). It started to rain (5) so we went inside. We ate some hot porridge (6) to warm up.

Mapping "Looby Loo"

RESOURCE MASTER

Which section of the song is it?
Write **A** or **B** in the box.

 *Refrain:* Here we go looby loo
Here we go looby light
Here we go looby loo
All on a Saturday night.

 *Verse:* I put my right hand in
I take my right hand out
I give my hand a shake, shake, shake
And turn myself about.

Refrain: Here we go looby loo
Here we go looby light
Here we go looby loo
All on a Saturday night.

Writing 1, 2, 3, 4, 5

RESOURCE MASTER R•24

Sing the song on page 103 of your textbook.
Clap the rhythm.
Draw in the note heads.
Write the pitch names.

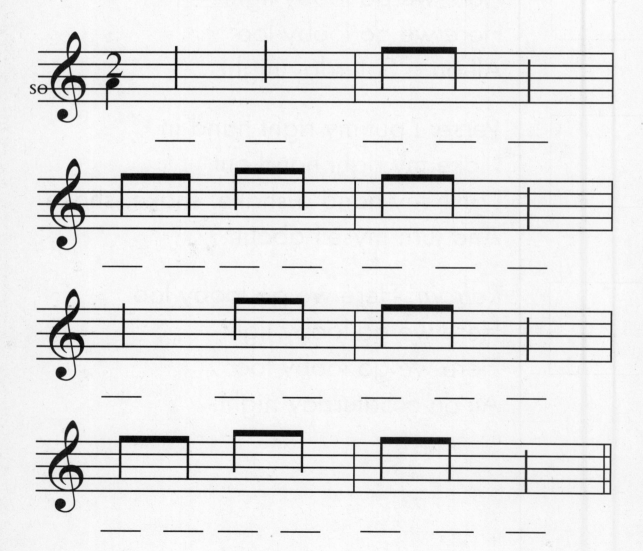

ABA Form

Cut out the pieces from "One, Two, Three, Four, Five." Paste the pieces under the right part of the song.

Six,   sev - en,   eight,   nine,   ten.

Then   I   let   him   go   a - gain.

Why   did   you   let   it   go?
Which   fin - ger   did   it   bite?

Be - cause it   bit   my   fin - ger   so!
The   lit - tle   fin - ger   on   my   right!

One,   two,   three,   four,   five.

Once   I   caught   a   fish   a - live.

Part A   Part B

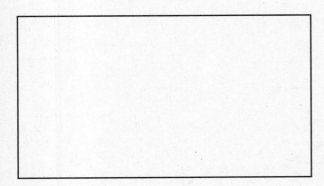

Curwen Hand Signs

RESOURCE MASTER R•26

do

ti

la

so

fa

mi

re

do

Name _____ Date _____

Pitch Ladder

Pitch Xylophone

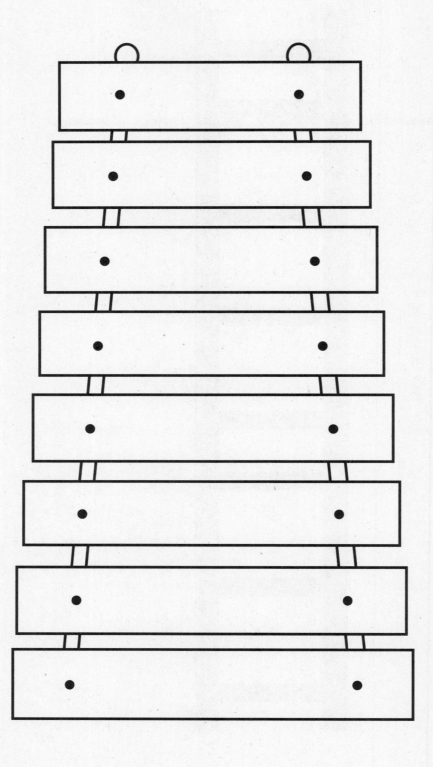

Name _____ Date _____

Beat Bars

Pitch Stairs

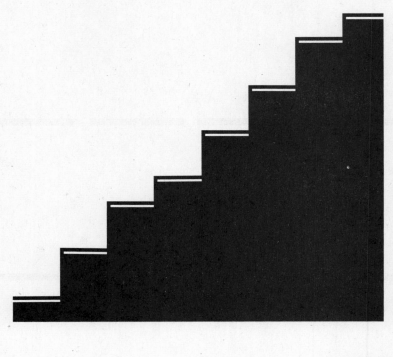

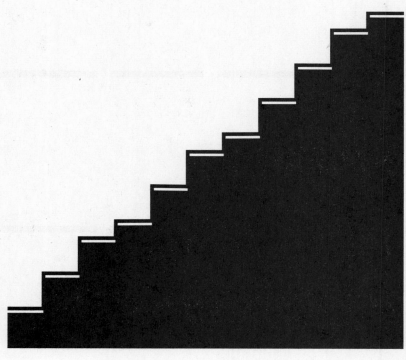

A Year with Frog and Toad Junior

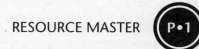
RESOURCE MASTER P•1

Music by Robert Reale   Book and Lyrics by Willie Reale
Based on the books by Arnold Lobel

Cast

Narrator	**Bees**
Children	**Birds**
(in three groups)	**Snail**
Frog	**Animal Friends**
Toad	**Squirrels**

Song 1: A Year with Frog and Toad

CHILDREN: The sun is out.
The sky is clear.
We came back.
Spring's almost here!
So let's begin a year with Frog and Toad.

The sun is out.
The sky is clear.
We came back.
Spring's almost here!
So let's begin another year.
A year with Frog and Toad.

(Shout) A year with Frog and Toad!

End of Song

NARRATOR: Once upon a time, there were two best friends.

(FROG and TOAD step out of the line and shake hands.)

And their names were Frog and Toad. They both hibernated through the winter.

(FROG and TOAD go to opposite sides of the stage, lie down, and put blankets over their heads.)

But soon, April came. And when April comes . . . what happens?

CHILDREN: It's time to wake up!

(We see FROG wake up, stretch, and go to TOAD, who is in his bed with the covers pulled tightly over his head.)

NARRATOR: Frog was very happy to get up and greet the spring. But did Toad get up?

CHILDREN: NO!

(FROG tries to wake up TOAD again, but it doesn't work.)

NARRATOR: Toad was very stubborn, and Frog needed some help!

CHILDREN: Wake up, Toad! It's springtime!

TOAD: It's springtime?

(Leaping out of bed and stretching.)

Why didn't you say so?

(They all sing.)

Song 2: Spring

ALL: Smell the flowers.
See the plants.
Hear the marching of the ants.

Feel the sunshine.
Feel the breeze.
Look out Frog,
Here come some bees.

Listen to the birdies sing.
Tweet tweet tweet.
Let's greet the Spring.
Let's greet the Spring.
It's Spring.
Spring!

End of Song

NARRATOR: One day, Toad and Frog both checked their mailboxes. Toad told Frog he never got any letters, and that made him really sad. Frog didn't want his best friend to be sad, so he wrote Toad a letter himself! And guess who Frog asked to deliver the letter for him?

BEES: The bees?

NARRATOR: No . . .

BIRDS: The birds?

NARRATOR: No . . .

ALL: The SNAIL!

(FROG hands the letter over to the SNAIL, and pats him on the back.)

NARRATOR: That's right! And the Snail promised to deliver it as fast as he could!

Song 3: Snail with the Mail

ALL: He's the snail with the mail.
He'll deliver without fail.
In the rain or sleet or snow.

No snail has feet more fleeta,
Why he's practica'ly a cheetah.
He puts the go in escargot!

He's the snail with the mail.
He'll deliver without fail.
In the rain or sleet or snow.

No snail has feet more fleeta.
Why he's practica'ly a cheetah.
He puts the go in escargot!

End of Song

NARRATOR: Frog and Toad and all their friends had so much fun during the springtime. You wouldn't believe all the things they did! Things like . . .

CHILDREN GROUP 1: Planting gardens!

CHILDREN GROUP 2: Flying kites!

CHILDREN GROUP 3: Having picnics!

NARRATOR: The days flew by, and soon it was summer! And what are some wonderful things about summer?

CHILDREN GROUP 1: Swimming!

CHILDREN GROUP 2: Games!

CHILDREN GROUP 3: Lemonade!

NARRATOR: That's right! And what goes perfectly with a tall, cool, glass of lemonade?

ALL: COOKIES!

NARRATOR: Exactly! And one sunny summer day, Toad baked some cookies to share with his friend Frog after dinner.

(We see TOAD baking cookies.)

But do you think Frog and Toad could wait that long to eat all the cookies?

ALL: NO!

NARRATOR: That's right! After all, what fun is baking cookies if you can't share them with all of your friends?

ALL: Mmmm! Yum!

Song 4: Cookies

CHILDREN: Eating cookies, eating cookies.
I'm so happy eating cookies.
Cookies, cookies, cookies I adore.
Cookies, cookies, cookies, cookies.
I go kooky eating cookies.

NARRATOR: Maybe you should stop.

CHILDREN: Just one more.

Eating cookies, eating cookies.
I'm so happy eating cookies.
Cookies, cookies, cookies I adore.
Cookies, cookies, cookies, cookies.
I go kooky eating cookies.
We will never stop.
Let's have more.

Cookies!!!

End of Song

NARRATOR: Autumn came and leaves started falling from the trees. Frog decided he wanted

134

to surprise Toad by raking up all the leaves in his yard. But what Frog didn't know is that TOAD had the exact same idea!

So both of them got some of their animal friends to help them, and everyone worked hard until there were two neat piles of leaves.

(All the ANIMALS stand back and admire their handiwork.)

Two neat piles . . . till the squirrels came. And did those squirrels help the other animals?

ALL: NO!

(All the SQUIRRELS mess up the piles, laughing mischievously as the other animals shake their heads.)

NARRATOR: They messed up both the piles. But in the end, what did Frog and Toad learn?

ALL: IT'S THE THOUGHT THAT COUNTS!

(The SNAIL moves forward.)

NARRATOR: That's right! And meanwhile, guess who was STILL trying to deliver Frog's letter to Toad?

ALL: Go, Snail, go!

NARRATOR: The Snail took so long that it became winter. And what do we do in the winter?

CHILDREN GROUP 1: Drink hot chocolate!

CHILDREN GROUP 2: And put on mittens!

CHILDREN GROUP 3: And play in the snow!

(All the ANIMALS begin shivering, and putting on scarves and hats.)

NARRATOR: That's right! One day, Frog asked Toad if he wanted to go sledding.

(We see FROG talking to TOAD, who doesn't want to go sledding. The other ANIMALS mime dragging their sleds up the hill.)

At first Toad was scared, but Frog told him everything would be OK.

(To the ANIMALS)

Ready, everybody?

ALL: READY!

NARRATOR: Then away we go!

Song 5: Down the Hill

ALL: Down the hill
We are sliding.
Down the hill
Gently gliding.

Down the hill!
What a thrill!
So exciting!
It's a thrill to be riding
Down the hill.

(The following dialogue is underscored.)

NARRATOR: . . . But everything was NOT OK! The hills grew steeper, and the sled started going faster and faster!

CHILDREN GROUP 1: Hold on, Frog!

CHILDREN GROUP 2: Hold on, Toad!

ALL: *(CONTINUED)*
Down the hill going faster.
Heading straight for disaster.

Down the trees.
Watch the boulders.
Tuck your knees
to your shoulders.

TOAD: Aaaaaaah!

End of Song

NARRATOR: Frog fell off the sled, leaving Toad all alone. This made Toad so angry that he said he was never going to speak to Frog again! But just then, guess who arrives?

CHILDREN: THE SNAIL WITH THE MAIL!

NARRATOR: That's right! The Snail gave Toad the letter, who read it. He realized how much Frog cared about him, and that they were best friends after all!

(The CHILDREN cheer.)

Before they knew it, it was time to hibernate for the winter once more.

(FROG and TOAD put on their sleep hats and get into bed.)

CHILDREN GROUP 1: Goodnight, Frog!

CHILDREN GROUP 2: Goodnight, Toad!

NARRATOR: Frog and Toad went to sleep and dreamed of all the adventures that awaited them in the spring. And guess what? Before they knew it, spring was here again. And when springtime comes . . . do you remember what happens?

(The ANIMALS throw off their winter hats, etc., as FROG and TOAD wake up.)

ALL: IT'S TIME TO WAKE UP, FROG AND TOAD!!!

(FROG and TOAD wake up once more, stretch.)

Song 6: A Year with Frog and Toad Reprise

ALL: The sun is out.
The sky is clear.
We came back.
Spring's almost here!
So let's begin a year with Frog and Toad.

The sun is out.
The sky is clear.
We came back.
Spring's almost here!
So let's begin another year.
A year with Frog and Toad.

(Shout) A year with Frog and Toad!

End of Song

Jump or Jiggle

Play the musical patterns below when you see the symbol in the poem.

 Güiro

 SX/AX

 Tamb.

 Ji. Bl.

 AG

 WB

Mar.

 Whistle

 Tri.

 V. Slap

 HD

 Slap Stick

 Conga

 Clvs.

The Rabbit in the Moon RESOURCE MASTER P•3

Play the musical patterns below when you see the symbol in the story.

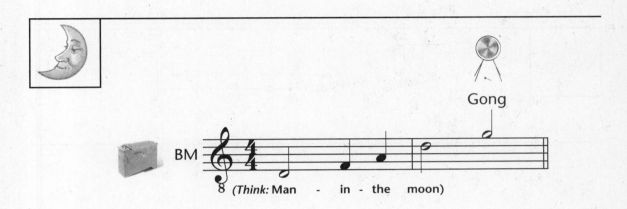

BM (Think: Man - in - the moon)

Gong

BX (Think: I am a sneak - y fox.)

AG (Think: Hop, hop, hop, hop, stop.)

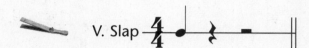 AX

(Think: I am a mon-key. You can't catch me.)

 V. Slap

 Tri.

WB

 AG/BM

USE WITH GRADE 1, STORIES TO PERFORM

Name _____ Date _____

Give From Your Heart

RESOURCE MASTER

Words and Music by
Cristi Cary Miller

Voice — Give of your-self; give from the heart.

AG/SG

AM

BM

Kind-ness will show right from the start. Give of your-self;

that's what to do. Love will come back to you.

Why the Beetle Has a Gold Coat

Play the musical patterns below when you see the symbol in the story.

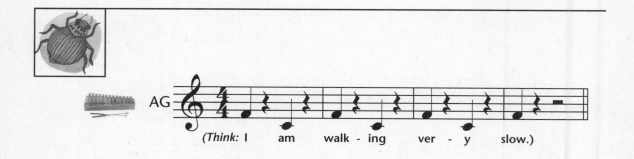

(Think: I am walk - ing ver - y slow.)

(Think: I am run-ning ver - y, ver - y fast.)

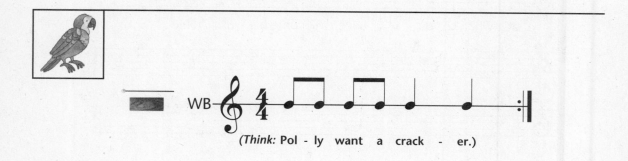

(Think: Pol - ly want a crack - er.)

Gong

Slap Stick

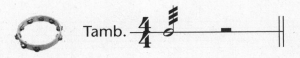

Tamb.

Cowbl.

Hidden Talents Rare

Words and Music by
Cristi Cary Miller

Voice: Judge not friends by how they look.

They have more to share.

Eyes a-lone can nev-er see their hid-den ta-lents rare.

Patriotism

Look at the flag. It is an important symbol of the United States. We are proud of our flag.

1. What shapes do you see? Circle your answers.

2. How many colors are used on the flag? _____

3. How many stripes are on the flag?
   Count them!   _____

Color them. Use an AB pattern: red, white.

Autumn Movement

Read the poem.

Fall is here.
Cold wind blows near.
The tree is so tall!
But the leaf must fall—
Down, down,
To the ground.
Moving and spinning,
It leaves me grinning!

Can you move like a falling leaf?
Make a dance.

150

Guitar or Violin?

Hispanic music uses many string instruments.
Here are two string instruments. Name the parts.
Use these words.

Guitar   Violin

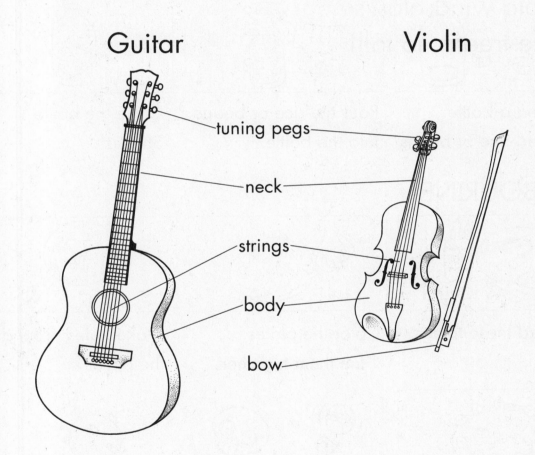

tuning pegs

neck

strings

body

bow

What is the same about the guitar and the violin?
What is different?
Talk about it with your class.

Scary Instruments

Make an instrument using everyday things.
Rattle like a skeleton!

MARACAS

You need a bottle.
You need rice or beans.

Pour the rice or beans into the bottle.

Close the bottle.
Shake!

TAMBOURINE

  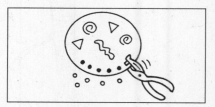

You need these things.

Color the plates.
Glue them together.

Make holes around the plates.

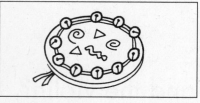

Add the jingle bells.
Shake!

Happy Halloween!

Thanksgiving Jumble

RESOURCE MASTER C•5

Find the Thanksgiving words.
Circle each word.

```
T H A N K S I N G P
U C R E C O R N A I
R F E A T H E R T E
K S T U F F I N G N
E C R A N B E R R Y
Y F A M I L Y A M K
```

| FEATHER | TURKEY | FAMILY | STUFFING |
| THANKS | CRANBERRY | CORN | PIE |

Sounds of Winter

1. Which words rhyme? Circle them.

    "It's So Nice on the Ice"

2. Look at the other long *i* words. Write the two that rhyme.

    _____ _____

| fine | hike | pile |
| pine | white | wide |

3. Glide and slide in long movements across the room.

Hanukkah

Did you learn a lot about Hanukkah?

Label each picture. Use the words in the box.

1.

_____

2.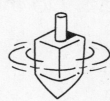

_____

3.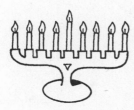

_____

4.

_____

menorah	latkes
gelt	dreidel

Kwanzaa Rhythm

Play a fun clapping game.

Form a circle. Do these things.

1

2

3

4

Keep the rhythm going.

Choose someone to start. That person says the name of the person to the left.

Keep the beat! Take turns around the circle.

Dr. Martin Luther King, Jr.

RESOURCE MASTER

Complete the paragraph about Dr. Martin Luther King, Jr. Fill in the blanks with the missing words.

colors	dream	equal	fighting

Martin Luther King had a big _____.

He wanted to help black people have

_____ rights. He didn't believe

in _____. He wanted

people of all _____ to live

in peace.

Chinese Mural

Chinese New Year is a spring festival. Make a mural to celebrate. A mural is a big picture for the wall.

First, create a dragon. Use red, yellow, and green.

Add flowers, oranges, and red lanterns all around the dragon.

Use glitter, crepe paper, and ribbons, too!

Your dragon represents power, luck, and success.

Listening Map Instructions

Instructions for LM-2 Hoo, Hoo!

Use with Unit 2, Lesson 2

Distribute a copy of the listening map to each student. Ask students what an echo is and have them do an imitation of an echo. Separate the class in to two halves and have each side echo back words or phrases to one another. Tell them that in this song, a boy is wondering who is answering back to him. Play the song and have students follow along with the map. After they listen, ask them who is answering back in the song.

Instructions for LM-3 John the Rabbit

Use with Unit 2, Lesson 7

Distribute a copy of the listening map to each student. Point out the two columns, one with the farmer, the other with the rabbits. Tell students that the song has two parts as well, the part the farmer sings and the part the rabbits sing. Every time the farmer sings, the rabbits sing back to him. As the students listen to the song, have them point to the appropriate column following the lyrics of the song. Another activity to do with this song would be separating the class into "farmers" and "rabbits" and have them sing their respective parts along with the recording.

Instructions for LM-4 Over in the Meadow

Use with Unit 2, Lesson 8

Distribute a copy of the listening map to each student. The lines on the listening map show the melody going higher and lower. On the first listening, have the students follow the melody lines with your guidance. Then have students cut out the pictures of the turtle, fish, and bird. Students could color these pictures if desired. As they listen to the three verses, they will use the pictures to move along the melody lines.

Instructions for LM-5 Jump, Jim Joe

Use with Unit 3, Lesson 1

Distribute a copy of the listening map to each student. Point out the beat bars at the top of the page. Have students use the beat bars to say the words out loud in the correct rhythm. Tell students that the song's lyrics are actually the directions for a game. Preview the map, pointing out how the words to the song match the game the children in the pictures are playing. Play the song, and have students follow the pictures on the map and sing along with the lyrics. After students have used the listening map, play the song again and have the students actually play the game that is described in the song.

Instructions for LM-7 Skip to My Lou

Use with Unit 3, Lesson 5

Distribute a copy of the listening map to each student. Point out the important concepts for each picture: buttermilk and fly, blue wagon, a girl who is without a partner, girl choosing partner. Explain to the students that the map is going to be used to help them remember the order

Listening Map Instructions

of the verses in the song. Play the selection and have the children point at the picture that corresponds with the verse being sung.

Instructions for LM-10
Tinker, Tailor

Use with Unit 4, Lesson 3

Distribute a copy of the listening map to each student. Have children follow along, pointing to each picture and identifying which picture is higher and which is lower for each pair. Sing the song with so and mi as a student points to each picture. Which tone is "Thief," so or mi? (so) Can they guess what each of these words means by looking at the picture? Ask why there is only one picture for the word "Thief" (because it only has one sound/syllable).

Instructions for LM-11
Walking the Dog
from *Shall We Dance*
by George Gershwin

Use with Unit 5, Lesson 3

Distribute a copy of the listening map to each student and have them listen to the music as they look at the pictures. Can they hear the sections that sound the same? Can they tell when the music changes and how the pictures change to match the music? (ABA coda).

Instructions for LM-12
Lavender's Blue

Use with Unit 5, Lesson 5

Distribute a copy of the listening map to each student. Before playing the song, review how the beat bars are used to

show the rhythm of the song. Ask how many beats there are in each measure (3). Ask students how they know there are three beats (they can either count the beat bars for the measure or they can look at the "3" on the top of the time signature. As students listen to the song, have them tap their fingers in a steady rhythm of 3. That means they will tap once for most syllables in the song; The word "dilly" is sung with two eighth notes, so students will tap only once for the two syllables. The words "green" and "queen" are dotted quarters, so students will tap three times on each of those words.

Instructions for LM-13 There's a Hole in the Middle of the Sea

Use with Unit 5, Lesson 6

Distribute a copy of the listening map to each student. This song has a lot of verses, and it may be difficult for some students to remember what lyrics come next. Tell students that they can use the listening map to help them remember the words to the song and keep the order straight. Tell them they can either follow the words or the pictures. Play the song and have students sing along, pointing at the picture that corresponds to the words in the song. After students have used the listening map, challenge them to sing the song by memory.

160

Listening Map Instructions

Instructions for LM-14
Goin' to the Zoo

Use with Unit 6, Lesson 1

Distribute a copy of the listening map to each student. Have students follow along as they listen to the words, identifying the **A** and **B** boxes. Have students echo you as you sing each line of the song. Each time they hear **A** ask students what is the same (melody and solo voice). Identify why **B** is different from **A** (different melody and group singing). Note that the words are different in the **A** section each time but the melody doesn't change. In the **B** section the words and the melody are the same each time.

Hoo, Hoo!

LISTENING MAP

There's someone living on a big, high hill, I wonder who it could be?
There's someone living on a big, high hill, who always answers me.

Hoo
Hoo

Hoo
Hoo

I wonder who it could be?

Name _____ Date _____

John the Rabbit
(American folk game song)

 Old John the Rabbit,  Oh, yes!

 Got a mighty bad habit,  Oh, yes!

 Of going to my garden,  Oh, yes!

 And eating up my peas,  Oh, yes!

 And cutting down my cabbage,  Oh, yes!

 He ate tomatoes,  Oh, yes!

 And sweet potatoes,  Oh, yes!

 And if I live,  Oh, yes!

 To see next fall,  Oh, yes!

 I won't plant,  Oh, yes!

 A garden at all!  Oh, yes!

Over in the Meadow
(American folk song)

LISTENING MAP

Jump, Jim Joe
(American folk song)

LISTENING MAP

part-   ner   **jump**

Jump, jump, jump, Jim Joe.

Shake your head   and nod your head   and tap your toes.

Round and round and round we go.

'till you find another partner
and you jump, Jim Joe

Skip to My Lou
(American play song)

LISTENING MAP

1. Flies in the buttermilk, shoo fly, shoo!

2. Little red wagon painted blue.

3. Lost my partner, what will I do?

4. I'll find another one, better than you.

5. Lou, lou, skip to my lou.

Tinker, Tailor
(traditional)

Walking the Dog
from *Shall We Dance*
by George Gershwin

LISTENING MAP LM•11

A

B

A

Coda

Lavender's Blue
(traditional English song)

 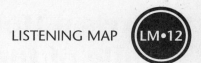

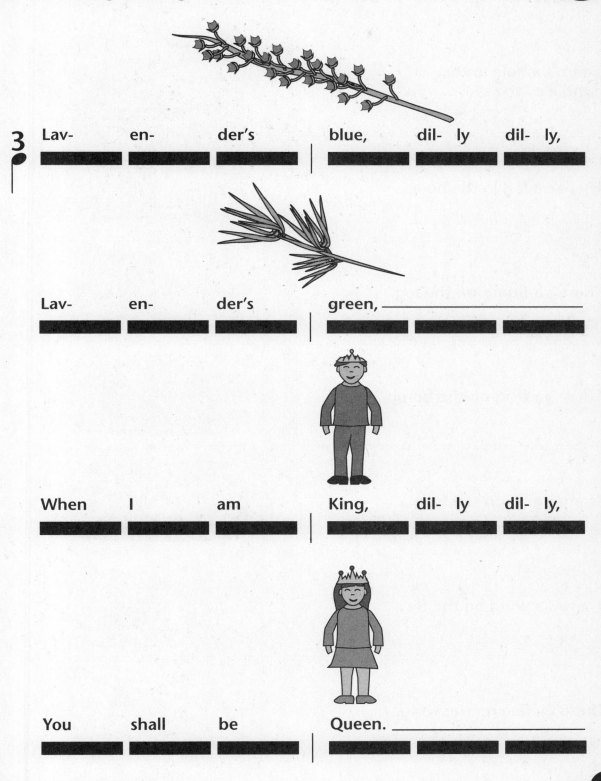

3

Lav- en- der's | blue, dil- ly dil- ly,

Lav- en- der's | green, _____

When I am | King, dil- ly dil- ly,

You shall be | Queen. _____

There's a Hole in the Middle of the Sea (singing game)

LISTENING MAP

There's a hole in the middle of the sea.

There's a log in the hole.

There's a bump on the log.

There's a frog on the bump.

There's a fly on the frog...

There's a wing on the fly...

There's a flea on the wing...

Name _____ Date _____

Goin' to the Zoo

A  | **B**

A  | **B**

A  | **B**

A  | **B**

A  | **B**

A  | **B**

Introduction to Signed Songs

by The Reverend Dr. Peggy A. Johnson, pastor
Christ United Methodist Church of the Deaf

The use of sign language along with vocal music has become a popular way of adding interest and expression to a song. Frequently a student who struggles with vocal music will find a successful outlet for expression through the use of sign language. Sign language has been used as an educational tool for reading comprehension and language development. Typically it appears as a picture for every spoken or written English word. This is known as "Signed English." It follows the grammar of English.

American Sign Language (ASL) is different from Signed English. It uses signs for words or concepts, but the grammar is produced with the eyes and face and through the movements of the body. It does not follow the word order of spoken English for the most part and has its own structure. ASL is the native language of people who describe themselves as Culturally Deaf. Deaf Culture is a community of people consisting of deaf and hard-of-hearing people who:

- use ASL,
- have primary personal relationships with people who also use this language,
- have typically attended state residential schools for the deaf where ASL is the mode of communication and instruction, and
- have unique history, traditions, and advocacy organizations.

For people in the Deaf Culture, ASL is used in their music and poetry, not Signed English.

It is difficult for a hearing person to sing an English word-order song and to sign in ASL at the same time. Most of the sign language section of this book is done in English word-order for that reason. However, some ASL grammar is incorporated for the purpose of linguistical awareness, and ASL grammar often creates a more artistic rendering of the movements. A phrase such as "lift up your eyes" in English would be best translated into ASL as "your eyes, lift up." The latter is more effective in a signed song because ending on a sign such as "lift up" has a better flow.

Hearing people who are fascinated by and attracted to signed music might consider taking a course on ASL. It would help increase one's skill in the language. People who study "foreign" languages often develop a sensitivity for the culture and people from which the language sprang. It is a sign of respect for the culture of the people for whom this language is their native language.

A good music program provides many benefits to students and teachers. Multicultural awareness is increased when we sing songs in Spanish or German or Japanese. By "singing" in ASL, students can gain multicultural awareness of the Deaf Culture.

Rules for Signed Singing

1) Every word does not need to be signed. Keep the signs flowing one to the other, and be sensitive to the length of the word in the music. The sign for a whole-note word should be stretched out longer and slower than a quarter-note word.

2) Right-handed and left-handed people sign opposite because there is a dominant, active hand and a passive hand in many signs. For a performance, it is best to have everyone signing one way or the other, either everyone do it right-handed or everyone do it left-handed.

3) When teaching a song, it is ideal to teach it with your back to the students facing a large mirror. In that way the directionality is correct. When a teacher faces a group of students and signs, the students tend to mirror the teacher, and then the sign goes in the opposite direction.

4) A person's face needs to be appropriate to the mood of the word being sung. "Sad" should look sad, "joyful" should look joyful, etc.

5) If at all possible, invite a native signer to assist with the teaching of the song. This shows respect for the Deaf Culture, and a live example of a sign is always preferable to a drawn picture of a sign in a book.

Perfection is not the goal. The joy of music expressed in sign language can occur even when the signs are not performed perfectly.

Alphabet and Numbers

MANUAL ALPHABET AND NUMBERS 1–10

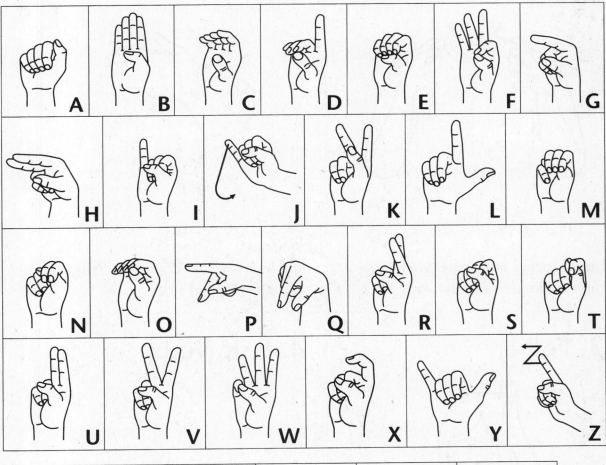

Plenty Fishes in the Sea (page 1)

SIGNING MASTER S•2

1. A lot (Plenty)

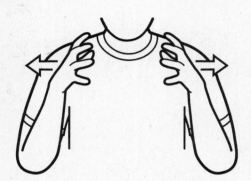

Hands facing each other with fingers curved. Hands move outward.

2. Fish (noun)

Hands in a "B" hand shape with the right hand in front of the left. Wiggle right side of hand side to side.

3. Father

Right hand in "5" hand shape with thumb touching forehead.

4. Fish (verb)

Both hands hold an imaginary fishing rod and shake slightly up and down.

Plenty Fishes in the Sea (page 2)

5. Mother

Right hand in "5" hand shape with thumb touching chin.

6. Cook

Left hand palm up receives the right hand. Right hand goes palm down on the left hand and then flips over to palm up on the left hand.

7. Baby

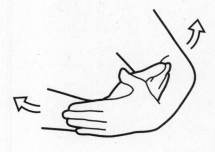

Hands and arms in a cradling motion from left to right.

8. Eat

Right hand in a closed position tapping the mouth in an eating motion.

Bonjour, Mes Amis (Hello, My Friends)

SIGNING MASTER S•3

1. Hello

Right hand in a "B" shape salutes from the brow of the right side of the head outward.

2. Friends

Both hands in an "X" shape with forefingers linking once with the right hand on top and then a second linking motion with the left hand on top.

3. Good

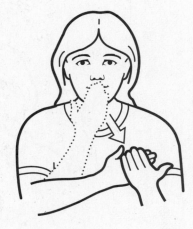

Right hand in a "B" shape beginning at the mouth and moving outward and landing in the palm of the left hand.

Willum (page 1)

1. Number 1

Right hand index finger in an upward position. The palm is facing out.

2. Number 2

Right index and middle fingers in an upward position. The palm is facing outward.

3. Number 3

Right index finger, middle finger, and thumb in an upward position. The palm is facing outward.

4. Number 4

All fingers extended in an upward position. Thumb tucked against the palm. The palm is facing outward.

Willum (page 2)

5. Number 5

The entire hand, fingers, and thumb extended in an upward position. The palm is facing outward.

6. Number 6

The right thumb and little finger join with the middle three fingers extending upward. The palm is facing outward.

7. Number 7

The right thumb and ring finger join with the other fingers extending upward. The palm is facing outward.

Library Song

1. Library

Right hand in the shape of an "L" with palm facing outward. The hand should make a circular motion with the "L."

2. Book

Both hands in a "B" shape with palms together and then separating them to a flat position like a book being opened.

3. Dictionary

The left hand in a "B" shape palm upward. The right hand in a "D" shape flicks the left hand as if turning pages.

Over in the Meadow

1. Dig

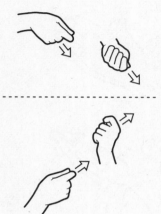

Both hands gripping an imaginary shovel, first diving downward and then pulling upward.

2. Swim

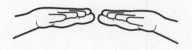

Begin with both hands in a "B" shape with palms facing downward and in front of the body. Make circular "swimming" motions with both hands.

3. Sing

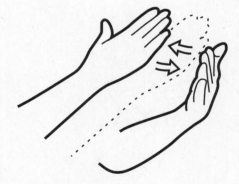

The left hand and arm are curved outward and stay stationary. The right hand, in a "B" position, swings back and forth across the left hand and arm.

Seeds

1. Joy

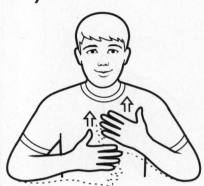

Make upward sweeps form the waist to the shoulders with both hands in a flat hand position with palms toward the body. The face should have a smiling expression.

2. Peace

Both hands are together with flat palms facing. The wrists turn the palms and then the palms separate to each side of the body with the palms facing downward.

3. Love

Hands are in a fist position and arms are crossed in front of the body like a hug.

Rattlesnake (page 1)

1. R

The right hand index and middle finger cross each other.

2. A

The right hand is in the shape of a fist with the thumb held to the side of the hand.

3. T

The right hand is in the shape of a fist with the thumb pointing up between the index and middle fingers.

4. L

The right thumb and index finger create the shape of an "L."

Rattlesnake (page 2)

5. E

The right hand's four fingers sit on top of the thumb that is laying against the palm of the hand.

6. S

The right hand is in the shape of a fist with the thumb gripping the front of the curled-under fingers.

7. N

The right hand index and middle fingers loop over the thumb that is laying against the palm of the hand. The ring finger and little finger and folded inward.

8. K

The right hand index and middle fingers are pointing upward, the other two fingers are closed toward the palm. The thumb points upward in between the index and middle fingers.

Rattlesnake (page 3)

9. Snake (Rattlesnake)

The right hand is in a letter "V" hand shape with the index and middle fingers curved and palm facing down. The right hand makes one quick striking motion outward with the hand.

Best Friends

1. Best

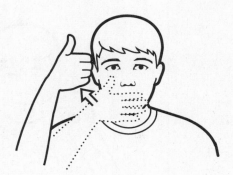

The right hand in a flat position with palm facing inward sweeps across the mouth and moves to the shape of a number "10" at the side of the head above the ear.

2. Friends

Both hands in an "X" shape with forefingers linking once with the right hand on top and then a second linking motion with the left hand on top.

Naughty Kitty Cat (page 1)

SIGNING MASTER S•10

1. Naughty

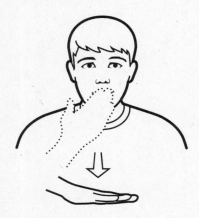

The right hand fingertips touch the mouth and then quickly swing away in a downward motion away from the body.

2. Cat

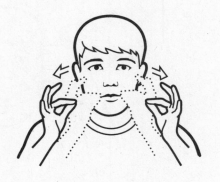

Both hands use their thumb and index finger to stoke imaginary whiskers from the cheek outward.

3. You

Index finger on the right hand points outward.

4. Fat

Both hands in a claw shape at the cheeks.

Naughty Kitty Cat (page 2)

SIGNING MASTER S•10

5. Butter

The left hand palm up receives two quick flicks of the index and middle finger of the right hand.

6. Whiskers (face)

The right hand index finger makes a circle around the face.

No One Like You (page 1)

1. Eyes

The right hand index finger points to first the right eye and then the left eye.

2. Nose

The right hand index finger points to the nose.

3. Mouth

The right hand index finger points to the mouth.

4. Ears

The right hand index finger points to the right ear.

No One Like You (page 2)

5. Hands

Both hands held out in front, palms down. The right hand palm brushes the back of the left hand and then the left hand palm brushes the back of the right hand.

6. Toes (Feet)

The right hand index finger points downward to the left and then the right foot.

7. Face

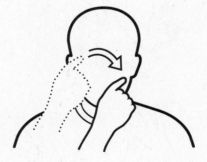

The right hand index finger makes a circle around the face.

The Happiest Street in the World

SIGNING MASTER S•12

1. Happy (joy)

Make upward sweeps form the waist to the shoulders with both hands in a flat hand position with palms toward the body. The face should have a smiling expression.

2. Street

The right and left hands held out to either side of the body with palms facing inward. The hands then move forward forming a path in front of the body

3. World

Both hands form a letter "W" and then the wrists circle each other in the front of the body ending with the right wrist on top of the left wrist.

Little Robin Red Breast

1. Thank you

Begin with both right and left hands with palms facing inward at the mouth. Come outward and away from the body.

2. For

The right index finger touches the forehead and then brings the finger away from the head dipping the finger down and then back up.

3. Tea

The left hand makes the shape of a sideways "O". The right hand makes a letter "F" and dips the "F" shape into the "O" in the left hand simulating a tea bag going into a cup.

Grade 1 Answer Key

Resource Master 1–4
Steady or Not?

Children should circle the windshield wipers and child walking. They should cross out the cat and the rain hitting the ground.

Resource Master 1–6
Rhythm Maze

Children should color in the footsteps that connect the clock and the heart.

Resource Master 2-4
Long or Short?

The LONG sounds box should contain pictures of the train, the fire truck, and the alarm clock. The SHORT sounds box should contain the pictures of the fingers, the owl, and the dripping water.

Resource Master 2-5
High or Low?

Children should color the bird, the whistle, the baby, and the mouse.

Resource Master 2-6
Arrows

Children should place the long arrows under *splash* and the short arrows under *pitter, patter.*

Resource Master 3-4
How Many Sounds?

Children should circle the 1 under the dog, the 2 under the monkey, the 1 under the bear, the 1 under the pig, the 2 under the tiger, and the 2 under the chicken.

Resource Master 3-5
Finding the Family

Children should paste the pencils under Woods, the spoons and the hubcap under Metals, the paper clips and keys under Shakers, and the garbage can under Drums.

Resource Master 3-8
Writing Rhythms

Resource Master 3-10
Create a Rhythm

Children should place a quarter note or two eighth notes above each beat bar to create their rhythms.

Grade 1 Answer Key

Resource Master 3-11
Think the Rhythm! Write It!

I like soda.

I like milk.

I like satin.

I like silk.

I like puppies.

I like kittens.

I like gloves.

I like mittens.

Resource Master 4-4
High or Low?

Children should write "H" under trumpet, violin, oboe, and bongos and "L" under tuba, string bass, bassoon, and timpani.

Resource Master 4-5
Fast or Slow?

Make sure that children are holding up the appropriate puppets as they listen to the music.

Resource Master 4-6
Lines and Spaces

Make sure that children place the notes on lines and on spaces in a similar fashion to the examples shown at the top of the page. Make sure that they also understand how to draw stems on the notes.

Resource Master 4-7
Writing *So* and *Mi*

Make sure that children have followed dotted guides to place *so* and *mi* in the correct places (D and B for the first exercise; C and A for the second exercise).

Resource Master 4-8
Write a *So-Mi* Melody

Answers will vary. Make sure that the melody each child writes is composed of the notes *so* (G) and *mi* (E) and that note stems are drawn correctly.

Resource Master 5-4
One or Two Beats

Lead children to copy the beat pattern from two of the lines in the song "In My Little Motor Boat."

Resource Master 5-6
Mi, So, and *La*

Children should paste *mi* on the short child, *so* on the middle child, and *la* on the tall child.

Resource Master 5-7
Word Beats

Children should circle the number 2 for table, 3 for elephant, 3 for computer, 3 for telephone, 2 for baby, and 2 for salad.

Grade 1 Answer Key

Resource Master 5-8
Pitty Patty Polt

Resource Master C-1
Patriotism

1. Children should circle the star, the square, and the rectangle.

2. 3

3. 13

Resource Master C-3
Guitar or Violin?

Discuss the similarities (same basic parts, members of string family) and the differences between the instruments (how they are held and played, their sounds).

Resource Master C-5
Thanksgiving Jumble

Resource Master C-6
Sounds of Winter

1. Children should circle *Nice* and *Ice*.

2. Children should write *fine* and *pine*.

Resource Master C-7
Hanukkah

1. latkes

2. dreidel

3. menorah

4. gelt

Resource Master C-9
Dr. Martin Luther King

Martin Luther King had a big **dream**. He wanted to help black people have **equal** rights. He didn't believe in **fighting**. He wanted people of all **colors** to live in peace.